Standards-Based

SCIENCE

Graphic Organizers & Rubrics
for Elementary Students

By Imogene Forte
and Sandra Schurr

Incentive Publications, Inc.
Nashville, Tennessee

Graphics by Joe Shibley and Jennifer J. Streams
Cover by Marta Drayton
Edited by Charlotte Bosarge

ISBN 0-86530-628-1

2   3   4   5   6   7   8   9   10   07   06   05

PRINTED IN THE UNITED STATES OF AMERICA
www.incentivepublications.com

Table of Contents

SECTION 1:
Directions for Using Graphic Organizers . . . 9

SECTION 2:
Graphic Organizers & Rubrics . . . 30

Appendix . . . 111

Index . . . 127

PREFACE

Recent research studies have confirmed a belief that intuitive teachers have long held germane to classroom success: when students are meaningfully involved in active learning tasks and in the planning and evaluation of their work, they are more enthusiastic about instructional activities, they learn and retain more, and their overall rate of achievement is greater. With the emphasis placed on measurable achievement as an overriding goal driving school system mandates, curriculum, classroom organization, and management (and even instructional practices and procedures), teachers are faced with great challenges. While striving to fulfill societal demands, they must also create and use new instructional strategies, procedures, and teaching methods to meet the diverse needs of students with widely varying backgrounds, interests, and abilities. In the rapidly changing world in which we live, and the growing avalanche of information, elementary science teachers are turning to student-centered instruction, active learning strategies, and authentic instruction to capture and hold students' interests and attention, and, consequently, result in increased achievement levels.

GRAPHIC ORGANIZERS

As the body of material to be covered in a given time frame grows more massive and multifaceted, and as content demands on students and teachers multiply, graphic organizers are becoming an important component of elementary science programs.

In the information-saturated classroom of today, sorting and making meaningful use of specific facts and concepts is becoming an increasingly important skill. Knowing where to go to find information and how to organize it once it is located is the key to processing and making meaningful use of the information gathered. Graphic organizers can be used to provide visual organization, develop scope and sequence, furnish a plan of action, aid in assessment, clarify points of interest, and/or document a process or a series of events.

The construction and use of graphic organizers encourages visual discrimination and organization, use of critical thinking skills, and meta-cognitive reflection. They can be particularly useful in helping elementary students grasp concepts and skills related to the seven standards established by the National Academy of Sciences.

In other instances, a graphic organizer may be developed as a reporting or review exercise or sometimes as a means of self-assessment after knowledge has been acquired. Graphic organizers can become valuable and effective instructional tools. The degree of their effectiveness for both students and teachers is determined by visual clarification of purpose, careful planning, organization, and attention to detail.

RUBRICS

Authentic assessment, as opposed to more traditional forms of assessment, gives both student and teacher a more realistic picture of gains made, facts learned, and information processed for retention. With rubrics, more emphasis is placed on the processing of concepts and information than on the simple recall of information. Collecting evidence from authentic assessment exercises, and taking place in realistic settings over a period of time, provides students and teachers with the most effective documentation of both skills and content mastery. Traditional measurements of student achievement such as written tests and quizzes, objective end-of-chapter tests, and standardized tests play a major role in the assessment picture as well.

The use of standards-based rubrics in elementary grade science classes has proven to be an extremely useful means of authentic assessment for helping students maintain interest and evaluate their own progress.

Rubrics are checklists that contain sets of criteria for measuring the elements of a product, performance, or portfolio. They can be designed as a qualitative measure (holistic rubric) to gauge overall performance of a prompt, or they can be designed as a quantitative measure (analytic rubric) to award points for each of several elements in response to a prompt.

Additional benefits from rubrics are that they require collaboration between students and teachers, are flexible and allow for individual creativity, make room for individual strengths and weaknesses, minimize competition, are meaningful to parents, allow for flexible time frames, provide multifaceted scoring systems with a variety of formats, can be sources for lively peer discussions and interaction, can include meta-cognitive reflection provisions which encourage self-awareness and critical thinking, and can help teachers determine final grades that are understood by (and hold meaning for) students.

NATIONAL STANDARDS

These standards-based graphic organizers and rubrics have been designed to provide busy elementary science teachers with a bank of resources from which to draw as the need arises. The seven standards developed by the National Academy of Sciences have been incorporated throughout all activities. For ease in planning, the Planning Matrix on pages 114-115 provides a complete correlation of activities to these standards.

Section 1:
Directions for Using Graphic Organizers

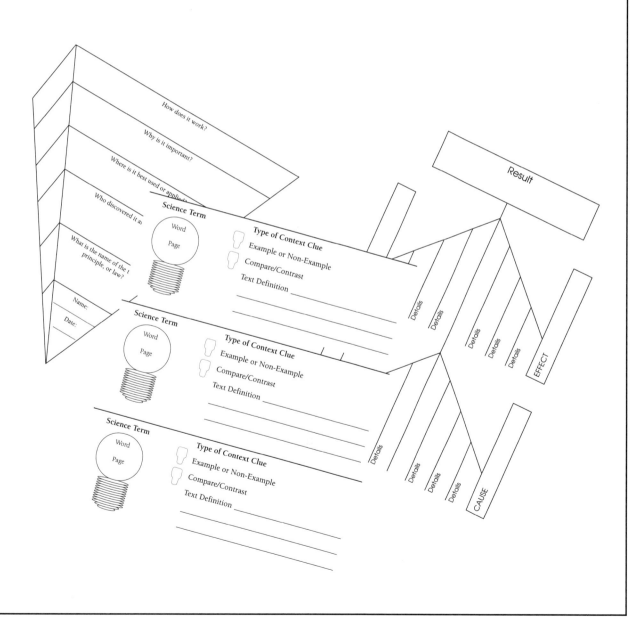

A+ Project Planning Guide

When carefully developed, this A+ Project Planning Guide will provide a blueprint for completion of a high quality project in a timely manner. It may be adapted effectively for planning and completion of a project, demonstration, essay, report, research paper, speech, or portfolio entry.

A reproducible copy may be found on page 31. Correlated rubric for assessment purposes may be found on page 32.

Type of Project: _____

Title and Brief Description of Project: _____

_____

_____

_____

Beginning Project Date: _____

Ending Project Date: _____

Materials Needed: _____

_____

Major Objective: _____

_____

Plan of Action: _____

_____

_____

_____

Possible Problems to Overcome: _____

_____

_____

Anticipated Grade from Rating Scale: _____ Actual Grade: _____

Major Lesson(s) Learned: _____

_____

_____

_____

Attribute Grid

The Attribute Grid can be used to either analyze or compare and contrast different attributes, criteria, characteristics, or qualities of varied objects, events, places, or things. Note that the attributes, criteria, characteristics, or qualities are written across the top of the grid while the objects, events, places, or things are written down the side of the grid.

A reproducible copy may be found on page 33. Correlated rubric for assessment purposes may be found on page 34.

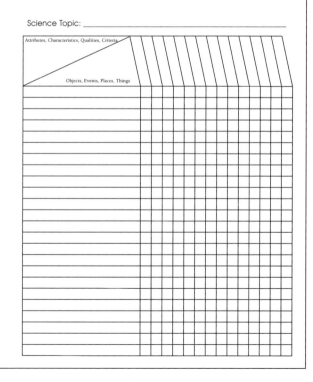

Science Topic: _____

Attributes, Characteristics, Qualities, Criteria

Objects, Events, Places, Things

Graphic Organizer

Bloom's Taxonomy Report Chart

After choosing a topic for an interesting science report or project, it is important to complete each of the tasks listed on the graphic organizer using Bloom's Taxonomy of Cognitive Development as the organizing structure. Keep in mind that these tasks are arranged in a scope and sequence so that each level progresses from lower-order thinking skills to higher-order thinking skills.
This graphic organizer can serve as a rough outline for recording key ideas that are included in a more comprehensive product.

A reproducible copy may be found on page 35. Correlated rubric for assessment purposes may be found on page 36.

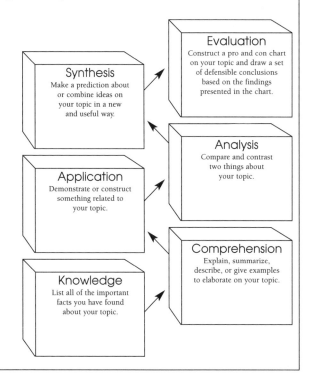

Graphic Organizer

Cause/Effect Fishbone Map

Science is the discipline of cause and effect from many points of view. It seems that for every action there is an equal and opposite reaction. (Which famous scientist said that?) This fishbone map is to be used for recording a series of science-oriented cause and effect situations that eventually lead to a result or set of results. Details should also be recorded where appropriate to do so.

A reproducible copy may be found on page 37. Correlated rubric for assessment purposes may be found on page 38.

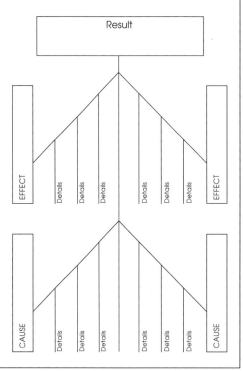

Graphic Organizer

Charting Science Skills

The Charting Science Skills Organizer is a good tool for students to use when completing a hands-on science activity to chart what they did and how they did it. This organizer may be used for experiments, observations, lab activities, investigations, or field studies.

A reproducible copy may be found on page 39. Correlated rubric for assessment purposes may be found on page 40.

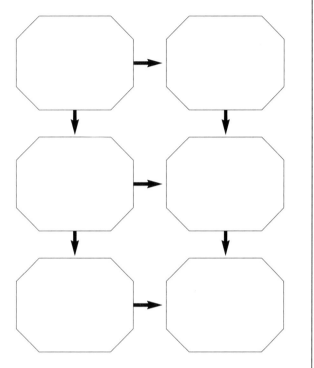

Graphic Organizer

Concept Builder

The Concept Builder is effective when the student wants to explore a science-related concept or big idea. The major concept is listed in the top circle, supporting ideas in the squares below the circle, and the important details or examples in the rectangles at the bottom.

A reproducible copy may be found on page 41. Correlated rubric for assessment purposes may be found on page 42.

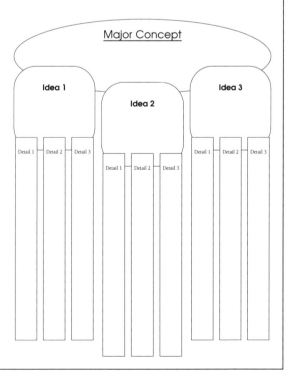

Standards-Based SCIENCE
Graphic Organizers & Rubrics for Elementary Students

Copyright ©2004 by Incentive Publications, Inc.
Nashville, TN.

Graphic Organizer

Context Clues

Science textbooks have many new and interesting terms to learn. One way a student can decipher these words is to use the Context Clues Organizer. There are three basic types of context clues which are in the form of examples or non-examples in comparison and contrast of ideas, or through specific textbook definitions. Students can use this organizer to figure out unfamiliar words in the textbook. Each unfamiliar science word is written inside the light bulb with its related page number and a check mark is written inside the box to indicate the source of its context clue.

A reproducible copy may be found on page 43. Correlated rubric for assessment purposes may be found on page 44.

Science Term
Word
Page

Type of Context Clue
Example or Non-Example
Compare/Contrast
Text Definition _____
_____
_____

Science Term
Word
Page

Type of Context Clue
Example or Non-Example
Compare/Contrast
Text Definition _____
_____
_____

Science Term
Word
Page

Type of Context Clue
Example or Non-Example
Compare/Contrast
Text Definition _____
_____
_____

Graphic Organizer

Cycle Graph

Cycles are very important to the study of science. This Cycle Graph Organizer requires students to record the various steps in an assigned cycle or in a cycle researched by the student. It should be noted that additional items can be inserted in the cycle if it requires more than four steps to complete.

A reproducible copy may be found on page 45. Correlated rubric for assessment purposes may be found on page 46.

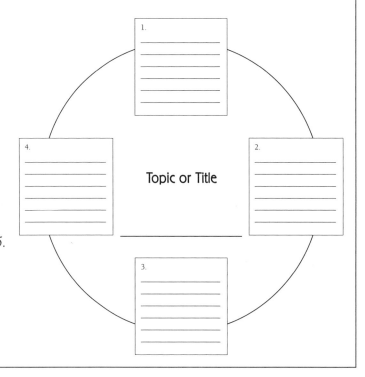

Topic or Title

Standards-Based SCIENCE
Graphic Organizers & Rubrics for Elementary Students

Graphic Organizer

Data Gathering Sheet for a Scientific Biography

Use the Data Gathering Sheet Organizer to record important birth information, early childhood and adult experiences, personal character traits/skills/interests/strengths, important discoveries/contributions, problems/difficulties encountered and overcome, as well as special awards/celebrations/tributes of an important scientist that has been assigned by the teacher or chosen by the student.

A reproducible copy may be found on page 47. Correlated rubric for assessment purposes may be found on page 48.

Name of Scientist, Date/Place of Birth, Date/Place of Death
Childhood Experiences
Personal Character Traits/Skills/Interests/Strengths
Problems/Difficulties Encountered and Overcome
Important Discoveries/Contributions/Awards and Tributes

Graphic Organizer

Discussion Guide

The Discussion Guide Organizer will help students prepare for any type of discussion that takes place in a science class. One way to do this is to record some answers to each of the questions suggested by the graphic organizer before participating in an active discussion group where students both trade information and hear what others have to say about the overall science topic assigned or agreed upon. This pre-planning effort provides the group with both a consistent agenda to follow and some ideas to share.

A reproducible copy may be found on page 49. Correlated rubric for assessment purposes may be found on page 50.

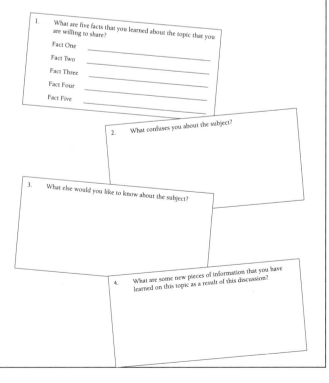

1. What are five facts that you learned about the topic that you are willing to share?
   Fact One
   Fact Two
   Fact Three
   Fact Four
   Fact Five

2. What confuses you about the subject?

3. What else would you like to know about the subject?

4. What are some new pieces of information that you have learned on this topic as a result of this discussion?

Event Outcome Graph

An Event Outcome Graph has both a horizontal axis and a vertical axis. This graph is used to record a series of scientific events that lead to a given set of outcomes or results. The events are recorded on the horizontal axis and the related outcome/result is recorded on the corresponding vertical axis.

A reproducible copy may be found on page 51. Correlated rubric for assessment purposes may be found on page 52.

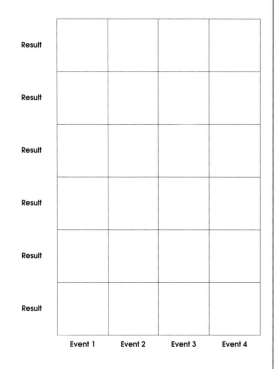

Experiment Form for Use with Any Science Topic

This graphic organizer is based on Gardner's Multiple Intelligences and requires the student to think of an experiment-related task or question to complete for each of the multiple intelligence areas. For example, here is a list of possible tasks for each of the multiple intelligences:

Verbal/Linguistic: Write a one-paragraph summary of your experiment.
Logical/Mathematical: Compare your experiment with a similar one done by another student.
Visual/Spatial: Draw a picture of something related to your experiment.
Body/Kinesthetic: Conduct a lab demonstration on some part of your experiment.
Musical/Rhythmic: Compose a jingle or cheer related to your experiment.
Interpersonal: Give a short talk explaining your experiment to others in the class.
Intrapersonal: Write a journal entry of questions/answers generated by your experiment.
Naturalistic: Point out the natural materials used as part of your experiment.

| Verbal/Linguistic |
| Logical/ Mathematical |
| Visual/Spatial |
| Body/Kinesthetic |
| Musical/Rhythmical |
| Interpersonal |
| Intrapersonal |
| Naturalistic |

A reproducible copy may be found on page 53.
Correlated rubric for assessment purposes may be found on page 54.

Graphic Organizer

Facts Only!

When students are taking notes while reading chapters in a textbook, doing research on the Internet, or reviewing information from a reference/multimedia source, it is important for them to have a consistent method of recording the factual information. A series of Facts Only! Organizers is a good way to handle this note-taking process. This graphic organizer provides students with a simple way to write down key ideas from their readings.

The individual pages can be stapled together to provide the students with an ongoing study guide booklet to be used when reviewing information for a science test or quiz.

A reproducible copy may be found on page 55.
Correlated rubric for assessment purposes may be found on page 56.

Main Fact

Supporting Facts
1. _____
_____
2. _____
_____
3. _____
_____
4. _____
_____
5. _____
_____
6. _____
_____

Graphic Organizer

Famous Person Chart

A Famous Person Chart depicts the personality traits, actions, and accomplishments of a well-known historical or famous figure in science who is described and discussed in the reading of a fiction/nonfiction book, a textbook selection, or a newspaper/magazine article. Important pieces of information are recorded on the outline of the character as a visual record of major accomplishments of this person through words, actions, and deeds.

A reproducible copy may be found on page 57.
Correlated rubric for authentic assessment purposes may be found on page 58.

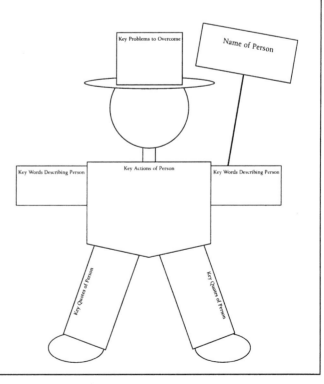

5 Ws and How of Scientific Theories, Principles, and Laws

An inverted pyramid figure is a type of diagram designed to help the student remember the five Ws (Who, What, When, Where, Why) and How of an important scientific theory, principle, or law. This graphic organizer is similar to the inverted pyramid often used in analyzing a newspaper article.

A reproducible copy may be found on page 59. Correlated rubric for assessment purposes may be found on page 60.

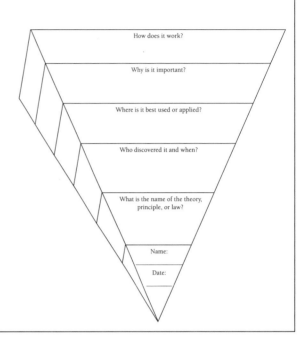

Flowcharting

Flowcharting is a good way to construct a sequence of events to explain a scientific process or phenomenon. A predetermined, universal set of flowcharting symbols in the form of different shapes, lines, and arrows are drawn to indicate different symbols and words in explaining this process or phenomenon. Flowchart symbols include everything from the recording of activities and events to problems, decisions, and alternatives.

A reproducible copy may be found on page 61. Correlated rubric for assessment purposes may be found on page 62.

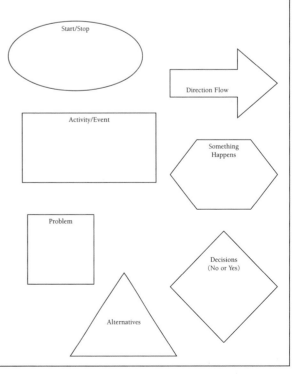

Grade A Science Project Planning Guide

The Grade A Science Project Planning Guide can be used to report on any science experiment activity required of the student. Bloom's Taxonomy of Cognitive Development is the organizing structure for recording the student's materials, procedures, data observed and collected, findings, conclusions, and results.

A reproducible copy may be found on page 63. Correlated rubric for assessment purposes may be found on page 64.

Knowledge: List the materials used in this experiment.
_____   _____
_____   _____

Comprehension: Outline the procedure for conducting the experiment.
1. _____
2. _____
3. _____
4. _____
5. _____

Application: Record data observed and collected during your experiment in chart or graph form.

What I Did	What I Observed
_____	_____
_____	_____
_____	_____

Analysis: Examine your data and draw conclusions.
1. _____
2. _____
3. _____

Synthesis: Create a series of "what if" statements about your data to show things that might be different should variables be changed.
What if . . . _____
What if . . . _____
What if . . . _____

Evaluation: Describe how you would rate the success of your experiment. Establish a set of criteria for measuring the results.

Findings	Measure of Success
_____	_____
_____	_____
_____	_____

Idea Organizer

Many controversial topics are presented in a science course for both discussion and debate. The Idea Organizer is used to write down key ideas, reasons, and conclusions that are generated during a small or large group dialogue. Rectangles are used to report both the reasons and conclusions while the ovals represent the key ideas in the topic for discussion or debate.

A reproducible copy may be found on page 65.
Correlated rubric for assessment purposes may be found on page 66.

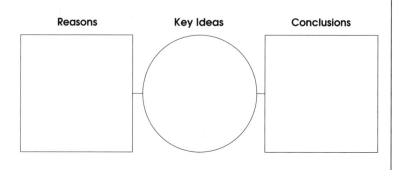

Reasons   Key Ideas   Conclusions

Graphic Organizer

Multiple Intelligence Data Organizer for a Science Project

The Multiple Intelligence Data Organizer is an excellent device to use when gathering data and input for a science-related project or presentation. It is suggested that the eight multiple intelligence areas serve as an organizing format when locating information on a topic of choice that is both relevant and varied from multiple points of view. The questions listed on the graphic organizer can serve as a guideline for beginning the recording process.

A reproducible copy may be found on page 67. Correlated rubric for assessment purposes may be found on page 68.

1. **Verbal/Linguistic Intelligence:** What books, magazines, newspapers, and other print materials are available for you to review?
   _____

2. **Logical/Mathematical Intelligence:** How can charts, graphs, diagrams, and technology tools help you gather information?
   _____

3. **Visual/Spatial Intelligence:** What pictures, photographs, maps, videos, posters, and other forms of visuals have information about the topic?
   _____

4. **Musical/Rhythmic Intelligence:** How might songs, raps, and audiotapes relate to your topic?
   _____

5. **Bodily/Kinesthetic Intelligence:** What computer software, Internet web sites, skits, dances, or physical/sporting events could serve you as reliable sources?
   _____

6. **Interpersonal Intelligence:** What family members, friends, teachers, experts, or community groups/organizations/institutions are there for you to interview in person, by telephone, or through chat rooms?
   _____

7. **Intrapersonal Intelligence:** What personal experiences, readings, feelings, opinions, or ideas on the topic do you have from which you could pull?
   _____

8. **Naturalist Intelligence:** How do Mother Nature and wildlife relate to your topic?
   _____

Graphic Organizer

Non-Fiction Book Report Outline

This Non-Fiction Book Report Outline is useful as an organizing structure for writing a creative nonfiction book report on any science topic. It is based on Bloom's Taxonomy of Cognitive Development and requires the student to share information on the Knowledge, Comprehension, Application, Analysis, Synthesis, and Evaluation levels of the taxonomy so that both lower- and higher-order thinking skills are reflected in the report itself.

A reproducible copy may be found on page 69. Correlated rubric for assessment purposes may be found on page 70.

Knowledge
1. Record the answers to each of these questions:
   What is the title of this book? _____
   Who wrote the book? _____
   When was the book published? _____
   Where did you locate the book? _____

Comprehension
2. Summarize the main ideas or facts found in the book.

Application
3. Select several key words or terms from the book and classify them in some way

Analysis
4. Compare your book with another book on the same topic. How are the books alike and how are they different?

Synthesis
5. Suppose that you were to write a new book on this topic. Create an original book jacket for your masterpiece.

Evaluation
6. Would you recommend the book to anyone else? Give three to five reasons for your choice.
   _____
   _____
   _____
   _____

Observation Log

An Observation Log is a collection of simple but informative entries about a given topic or subject. Observation logs are used to watch something closely over a period of time and to record the changes observed during this process. All entries require a date and time for the observation as well as a few sentences describing what is seen.

A reproducible copy may be found on page 71. Correlated rubric for authentic assessment purposes may be found on page 72.

Date: _____ Time: _____
Observation: _____
_____
_____
_____
_____
_____
_____
_____
_____
_____

Date: _____ Time: _____
Observation: _____
_____
_____
_____
_____
_____
_____
_____
_____
_____

Outline for Developing a Science Unit

Developing a science unit on a topic of one's choice is easier than most people think. Once a topic is chosen, the student or teacher selects one or more tasks from each level of Bloom's Taxonomy to create a teaching and learning unit of study. It should be noted that each level of the taxonomy provides three different task options to be incorporated within the unit itself.

A reproducible copy may be found on page 73. Correlated rubric for assessment purposes may be found on page 74.

Knowledge
1. List five to ten questions that you would like to answer about the topic.
2. Identify five to ten key words or terms related to the topic and write their definitions.
3. Name three to five specific sources for information about the topic.

Comprehension
1. Outline a plan for finding out all you can about the topic.
2. Summarize what you would like to know most about the topic.
3. Describe five to ten ways that you might share acquired information.

Application
1. Interview someone with knowledge of the topic.
2. Make a model to show something important about the topic.
3. Conduct an experiment to demonstrate a key idea related to the topic.

Analysis
1. Compare and contrast some aspect of your topic with that of another topic.
2. Divide your topic into several sub-topics.
3. Conduct your survey to show how others feel about the topic.

Synthesis
1. Create a list of predictions related to the topic.
2. Compose a poem or story about the topic.
3. Design a series of drawings or diagrams to show facts about the topic.

Evaluation
1. Determine the five most important facts you have learned about the topic. Rank them from most important to least important, giving reasons for your first choice.
2. Criticize a resource you used to find out more information about the topic and give at least three recommendations for improving it.

Panel Presentation Outline

A Panel Presentation Outline can be an excellent way to share information with a large group. When planning a panel presentation on a science topic, the organizing panel member should begin by choosing three or four people to serve on the panel, then choose a moderator whose job it is to both organize the panel's delivery of information and keep the panel's questions, answers, and comments moving along in a smooth and orderly fashion. The organizing panel member should also write down the topic of the panel presentation, the names and science concepts to be covered by each panel member, and some basic questions the panel moderator can use as needed to facilitate the discussion.

A reproducible copy may be found on page 75. Correlated rubric for assessment purposes may be found on page 76.

Topic for Panel _____

Name of Panel Moderator _____

Question 1: _____
Question 2: _____
Question 3: _____
Question 4: _____

Panel Member One
_____
_____
_____

Panel Member Two
_____
_____
_____

Panel Member Three
_____
_____
_____

Panel Member Four
_____
_____
_____

Picture/Graph Response Chart

It has been said many times that "a picture is worth a thousand words." The Picture/Graph Response Chart is designed to help the student record individual thoughts about any meaningful picture, photograph, illustration, drawing, diagram, chart, or graph that is encountered in a science textbook or reference book. The four major parts of this graphic organizer encourage the student to describe what they see, explain what they think is happening, tell why it is happening, and reasons why it was chosen for inclusion in this particular book.

A reproducible copy may be found on page 77. Correlated rubric for assessment purposes may be found on page 78.

Describe what you see.

Explain what is happening.

Tell why this is happening.

Give reasons why it was chosen for this book.

Position Paper Planner Outline

A position paper is a paragraph-oriented outline used to plan the major ideas and supporting details for a short but interesting report on a science topic. A Position Paper Planner is used to convince others how the author feels or reacts to a given situation. It is highly recommended to help the writer organize information researched on the topic. The introductory paragraph encourages the student to develop both an opening statement that catches the reader's attention as well as a comprehensive thesis statement. The body paragraphs require a topic sentence as well as three supporting sentences, and the concluding paragraph refers back to the opening paragraph and also includes a final statement in the form of a rhetorical question, point to ponder, or basis for further study.

A reproducible copy may be found on page 79.
Correlated rubric for assessment purposes may be found on page 80.

Introductory Paragraph
1. Eye-catching example, startling statement, personal anecdote, dramatic quotation, unusual data/fact to catch reader's attention:
2. Thesis Statement:

Body Paragraph One
1. Topic Sentence:
2. Supporting Sentence:
3. Supporting Sentence:
4. Supporting Sentence:

Body Paragraph Two
1. Topic Sentence:
2. Supporting Sentence:
3. Supporting Sentence:
4. Supporting Sentence:

Body Paragraph Three
1. Topic Sentence:
2. Supporting Sentence:
3. Supporting Sentence:
4. Supporting Sentence:

Concluding Paragraph
1. Concluding sentence based on thesis statement:
2. Final statement in form of rhetorical question, point to ponder, or basis for further study:

Prediction Chart

Making predictions is an important part of any science observation project, science experiment, science report, or science research study. This Prediction Chart will help the student structure his/her thoughts when completing a science assignment that calls for the act of making predictions. Both written comments and detailed drawings or sketches can be used for this purpose.

A reproducible copy may be found on page 81.
Correlated rubric for assessment purposes may be found on page 82.

Draw — What did you see happen?   **Write**

Draw — What will happen next?   **Write**

Draw — What else will happen?   **Write**

Problem-Solving Tree

This Problem-Solving Tree allows the reader visually to depict possible outcomes for any science-related problem under study. After charting various advantages and disadvantages to several different but potential solutions, a summary conclusion is written in the squares provided at the bottom of each solution figure.

A reproducible copy may be found on page 83. Correlated rubric for assessment purposes may be found on page 84.

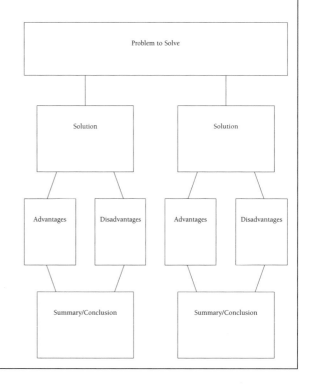

Prove the Hypothesis Chart

A Prove the Hypothesis Chart is an unproved theory tentatively accepted to explain certain facts. The chart can be used to record a student's notes when forming a hypothesis about a scientific idea, discovery, or experiment. When completing this chart, one must state the hypothesis, give statements of proof to either support or negate the hypothesis, and then summarize the opinion-proof notes in a concluding paragraph.

A reproducible copy may be found on page 85. Correlated rubric for assessment purposes may be found on page 86.

Hypothesis/Proof/Opinion Chart	
Hypothesis:	Proof Statements:
Opinion/Proof Notes and Conclusion	

Graphic Organizer

Research Guide

It is so important to establish a plan for guiding or regulating one's research on a science topic in order to make the data gathering process more manageable and readable. The Research Guide is an excellent research tool to use when planning a project or product. This graphic organizer has the students reporting on research concepts and ideas that need to be defined and/or explored, on research tools and sources to consider and investigate, as well as on a research plan and steps to take and complete.

A reproducible copy may be found on page 87. Correlated rubric for assessment purposes may be found on page 88.

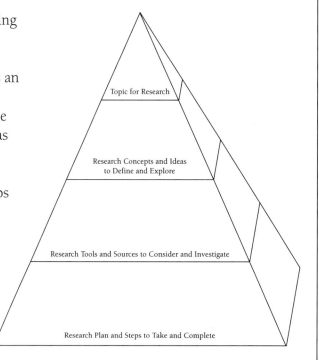

Graphic Organizer

Research Paper Outline

The Research Paper Outline will provide a carefully thought-out plan for completing a quality research paper. Special attention should be given to availability of time and materials in relationship to the researcher's goal.

A reproducible copy may be found on page 89. Correlated rubric for assessment purposes may be found on page 90.

I. Topic

II. Introduction

III. Background Information

IV. Materials and Sources

V. Resource People

VI. Procedures

VII. Investigations and Results

VIII. Discussion

IX. Conclusion and Summary

X. Bibliography

XI. Appendix

Graphic Organizer

Science Project Display Board Plan

The Science Project Display Board Plan helps the student record their ideas for a science fair or classroom science project. The large display board organizer provides spaces for the student to write down information about the project's purpose, problem/question, hypothesis, investigations/observations, results, materials, procedures, and conclusions.

A reproducible copy may be found on page 91.
Correlated rubric for assessment purposes may be found on page 92.

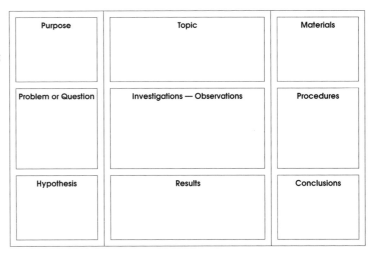

Purpose	Topic	Materials
Problem or Question	Investigations — Observations	Procedures
Hypothesis	Results	Conclusions

Graphic Organizer

Science Quilt

The five big sections of the Science Quilt Organizer may be filled in below to show five different sets of drawings that show some important facts about the report topic. For example, if information about an animal's habitat was being recorded, the student would draw a pattern of a simple object or icon to tell where the animal lives, a pattern of a drawing or icon that shows what the animal eats, another pattern to show how the animal protects itself, etc.

A reproducible copy may be found on page 93.
Correlated rubric for assessment purposes may be found on page 94.

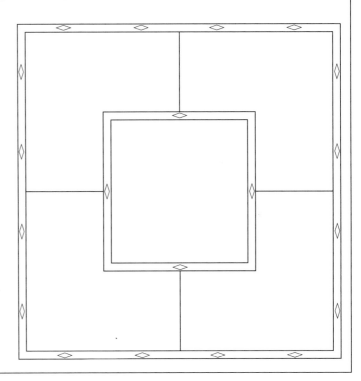

Scientific Categories and Their Relationships

The Scientific Categories and Their Relationships Organizer contains a series of circles and lines that enable the reader to visually see relationships among the established circles and lines. Once a scientific topic is chosen for study, it is important to list its subcategories and relationships in such a way that one is able to see a scope and sequence in the organizational structure.

A reproducible copy may be found on page 95.
Correlated rubric for assessment purposes may be found on page 96.

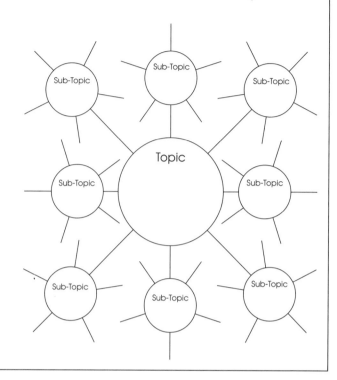

Scientific Terms Log

A Scientific Terms Log can be a useful tool for organizing terms important to any unit of study. Maintaining a log requires the student to record all of the important scientific words or terms from a unit of study by writing the word itself in the first box, defining the word in the second box, and illustrating the word (or using the word in a sentence) in the third box.

A reproducible copy may be found on page 97.
Correlated rubric for assessment purposes may be found on page 98.

Scientific Term	Definition of Term	Illustration/Sentence of Term

Study Guide for Preparing for a Science Quiz

This organizer will be helpful to a student when collecting, analyzing, studying, and reviewing notes. It will not only help to gather the main ideas, topics, and facts needed for the quiz, but it also will teach the student to formulate and maintain an organized study plan.

A reproducible copy may be found on page 99. Correlated rubric for assessment purposes may be found on page 100.

STUDY GUIDE

Topics to be Covered	Today's Date	Length/Format of Quiz
1. Major Topic	_____	
2. Subtopics	Quiz Date	
	_____	

Materials to be reviewed (textbooks, class notes, handouts)

Challenges to be expected and/or questions to answer

My Study Plan
1.
2.
3.
4.
5.
6.

Textbook Survey

A standard Textbook Survey template can be used to survey and write down the important facts from a textbook selection read by any student. For each paragraph, the student records the main fact given, a personal comment, reaction, or opinion about the stated fact, and a question to ask oneself as a memory device for remembering each fact.

A reproducible copy may be found on page 101. Correlated rubric for assessment purposes may be found on page 102.

Fact
Comment/Reaction/Opinion
Question

Fact
Comment/Reaction/Opinion
Question

Graphic Organizer

Time Line Template

It is important to decide on the important dates to record when investigating a scientific discovery, invention, event, or when researching the life of an important scientist from history. Specific events that go with each date should then be written down. This time line pattern can be extended as needed. One should also note that the vertical lines at the bottom of the graphic organizer can be used for additional notes or comments.

A reproducible copy may be found on page 103. Correlated rubric for assessment purposes may be found on page 104.

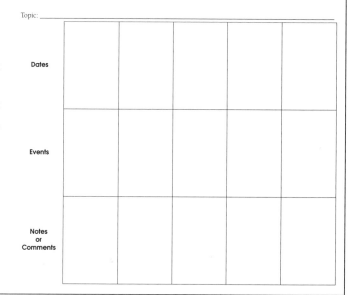

Graphic Organizer

Venn Diagram

A Venn Diagram consists of large intersecting circles that are used to compare and contrast different but related objects, concepts, or events. A Venn diagram can be useful when researching a topic that requires comparison and contrast. As one conducts research, it is important to look for interrelationships among topics. Areas of commonality should be recorded in the intersecting segments of the circles, while differences should be recorded in the appropriate non-intersecting segments of the circles.

A reproducible copy may be found on page 105. Correlated rubric for assessment purposes may be found on page 106.

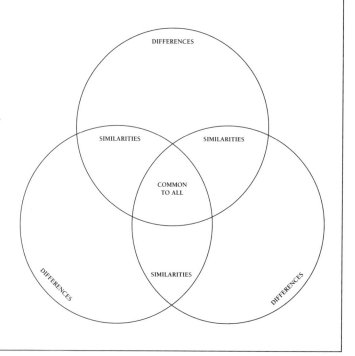

Standards-Based SCIENCE
Graphic Organizers & Rubrics for Elementary Students

Weather Observation Chart

The Weather Observation Chart may be used to keep track of the weather for a specified period of time. The symbols provided will make it easier to record daily information, but in some instances, it may be more interesting to devise original symbols (example: umbrella or raindrops for rain; dark cloud for thunderstorms; sunglasses for sun, etc.). The chart may be used as is for individual observations or enlarged as a bulletin board or chart of group use.

A reproducible copy may be found on page 107.
Correlated rubric for assessment purposes may be found on page 108.

Weather Symbols	Weather Observation Log							
WEATHER TYPE	Date	Time	Temperature	Weather Type	Cloud Cover	Wind Condition	Wind Chill Temperature	Forecast
Rain R								
Thunderstorm T								
Fog FG								
Smog SMG								
Frost FR								
Snow S								
CLOUD COVER								
Clear Skies								
Partly Cloudy								
Cloudy								
WIND CONDITIONS								
Calm (No air motion)								
Breezy (Leaves in motion, water rippled)								
Windy (Tree limbs moving, whitecaps on water)								
Very Windy (Tree trunks bend, water rough)								

What, So What, Now What? Chart

A What, So What, and Now What? Chart organizes one's thinking after reading a story, textbook section, or an article on a given topic by requiring reflection back over the information presented.

The *What?* column requires the student to write down a response to the question: What did I learn from this selection?

The *So What?* column requires the student to write down a series of responses to the question: What difference does it make now that I know this?

The *Now What?* column asks students to write down some thoughts answering the question: How can I use this information to make a difference in what I know or can do?

A reproducible copy may be found on page 109.
Correlated rubric for authentic assessment purposes may be found on page 110.

Topic of Study/Title _____

Student's Name _____

What?	So What?	Now What?

Standards-Based SCIENCE
Graphic Organizers & Rubrics for Elementary Students

Section 2:
Graphic Organizers & Rubrics

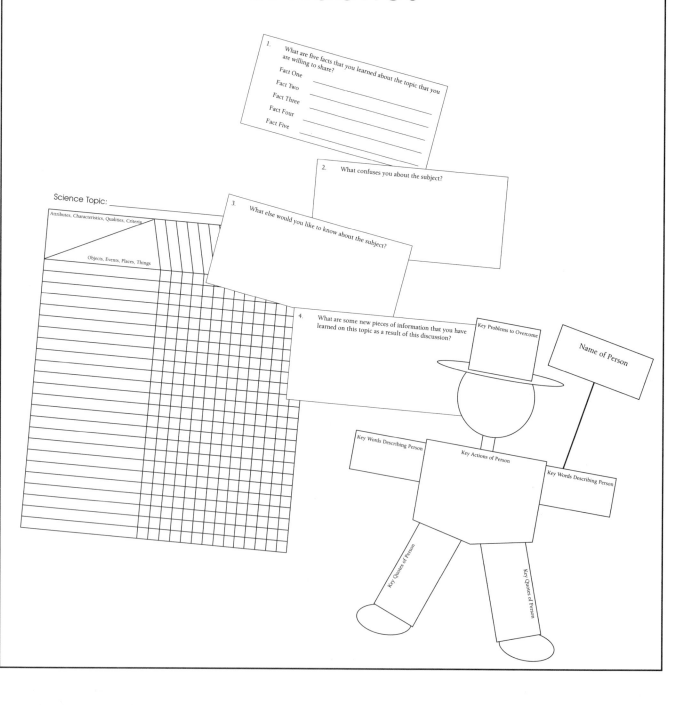

1. What are five facts that you learned about the topic that you are willing to share?

Fact One _____

Fact Two _____

Fact Three _____

Fact Four _____

Fact Five _____

2. What confuses you about the subject?

3. What else would you like to know about the subject?

4. What are some new pieces of information that you have learned on this topic as a result of this discussion?

Science Topic: _____

Attributes, Characteristics, Qualities, Criteria

Objects, Events, Places, Things

Key Problems to Overcome

Name of Person

Key Words Describing Person

Key Actions of Person

Key Words Describing Person

Key Quotes of Person

Key Quotes of Person

A+ Project Planning Guide

Graphic Organizer

Directions to Student:

Predict what grade you will receive on this project as you fill out the Project Planning Guide. Then, record your final grade after completing the information and tasks outlined on the Planning Guide.

Type of Project: _____

Title and Brief Description of Project: _____

_____

_____

_____

Beginning Project Date: _____

Ending Project Date: _____

Materials Needed: _____

_____

_____

Major Objective: _____

_____

_____

Plan of Action: _____

_____

_____

_____

Possible Problems to Overcome: _____

_____

_____

Anticipated Grade from Rating Scale: _____ Actual Grade: _____

Major Lesson(s) Learned: _____

_____

_____

_____

Standards-Based SCIENCE
Graphic Organizers & Rubrics for Elementary Students

A+ Project Planning Guide

Rating Scale:

A	B	C
Absolute Best	Better	Could Be Better

Directions to Student:

In the box at the end of each line, write the letter that best describes your performance on this activity.

1. I chose an appropriate topic for this project.	☐
2. I gave my project a good title and wrote a brief description of the subject.	☐
3. I began and ended the project in a timely fashion.	☐
4. I located the necessary materials to complete the project.	☐
5. I wrote the major objective for the project.	☐
6. I developed a plan of action for the project.	☐
7. I anticipated possible problems to overcome before starting the project and was able to resolve them to my satisfaction.	☐
8. My anticipated grade for the project matched the actual grade I received.	☐

Comments by Student: _____

_____

_____

_____

Signed _____ Date _____

Comments by Teacher: _____

_____

_____

_____

Signed _____ Date _____

Attribute Grid

Science Topic: _____

Attributes, Characteristics, Qualities, Criteria															
Objects, Events, Places, Things															

Standards-Based SCIENCE
Graphic Organizers & Rubrics for Elementary Students

Attribute Grid

Rating Scale: 3   2   1

                  I did it!   I almost did it!   I did some of it!

Directions to Student:

In the box at the end of each line, write the number that best describes your work.

WHAT I DID	HOW I DID
1. I was able to use this grid to analyze something.	☐
2. I was able to use this grid to compare and contrast something.	☐
3. I was able to use this grid to examine different attributes.	☐
4. I was able to use this grid to examine different criteria.	☐
5. I was able to use this grid to examine different characteristics.	☐
6. I was able to use this grid to examine qualities.	☐
7. I was able to use this grid to examine objects.	☐
8. I was able to use this grid to examine events.	☐
9. I was able to use this grid to examine places.	☐
10. I was able to use this grid to examine things.	☐

Comments by Student: _____

_____

_____

          Signed _____ Date _____

Comments by Teacher: _____

_____

_____

          Signed _____ Date _____

Bloom's Taxonomy Report Chart

Graphic Organizer

Evaluation
Construct a pro and con chart on your topic and draw a set of defensible conclusions based on the findings presented in the chart.

Synthesis
Make a prediction about or combine ideas on your topic in a new and useful way.

Analysis
Compare and contrast two things about your topic.

Application
Demonstrate or construct something related to your topic.

Comprehension
Explain, summarize, describe, or give examples to elaborate on your topic.

Knowledge
List all of the important facts you have found about your topic.

35

Bloom's Taxonomy Report Chart

Rubric

Topic: _____

Directions to Student:

Place an "x" in the box at the end of each line that shows your results on this activity.

	Great Evidence	Ample Evidence	Little Evidence
Knowledge: Evidence of learned facts, methods, procedures, or concepts.	☐	☐	☐
Comprehension: Evidence of understanding of facts, methods, procedures, or concepts.	☐	☐	☐
Application: Evidence of use of the information in new situations.	☐	☐	☐
Analysis: Evidence of analysis, recognition of assumptions, and evaluation of relevancy of information.	☐	☐	☐
Synthesis: Evidence of putting information together in a new and creative way.	☐	☐	☐
Evaluation: Evidence of acceptance or rejection of information on the basis of criteria.	☐	☐	☐

Comments by Student: _____

_____

_____

Signed _____ Date _____

Comments by Teacher: _____

_____

_____

Signed _____ Date _____

Standards-Based SCIENCE
Graphic Organizers & Rubrics for Elementary Students

Cause/Effect Fishbone Map

Graphic Organizer

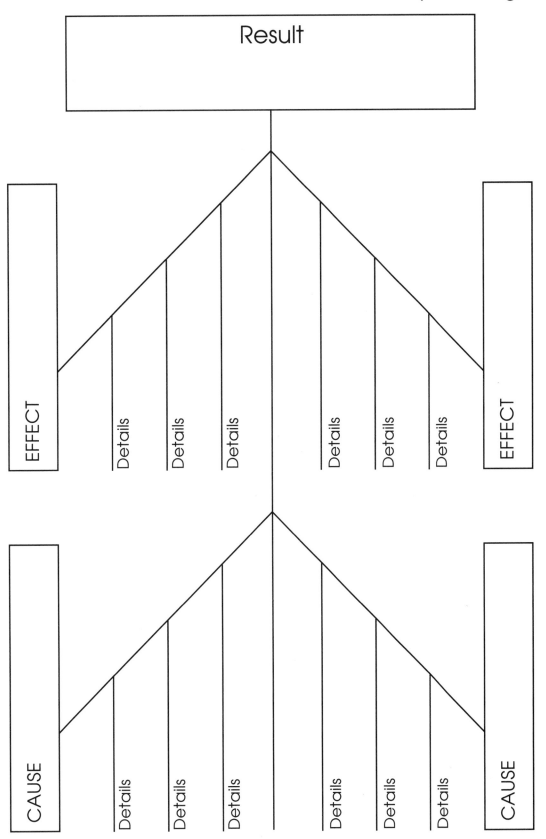

Result

EFFECT

Details Details Details Details Details Details

EFFECT

CAUSE

Details Details Details Details Details Details

CAUSE

Standards-Based SCIENCE
Graphic Organizers & Rubrics for Elementary Students

Cause/Effect Fishbone Map

Rubric

Rating Scale: **A**   **B**   **C**

                   Completely   Somewhat   Not At All

Directions to Student:

In the box at the end of each line, write the letter that best describes your performance on this activity.

1. I was able to find two causes to examine.	☐
2. I was able to find details to support the causes.	☐
3. I was able to use the details to determine the effects from the causes.	☐
4. I was able to successfully find the result.	☐
5. I understand the use of a Cause/Effect Fishbone Map.	☐
6. I can see how the Cause/Effect Fishbone Map could be used to predict outcomes.	☐

Comments by Student: _____

_____

_____

_____

_____

Signed _____ Date _____

Comments by Teacher: _____

_____

_____

_____

Signed _____ Date _____

Standards-Based SCIENCE
Graphic Organizers & Rubrics for Elementary Students

Charting Science Skills

Graphic Organizer

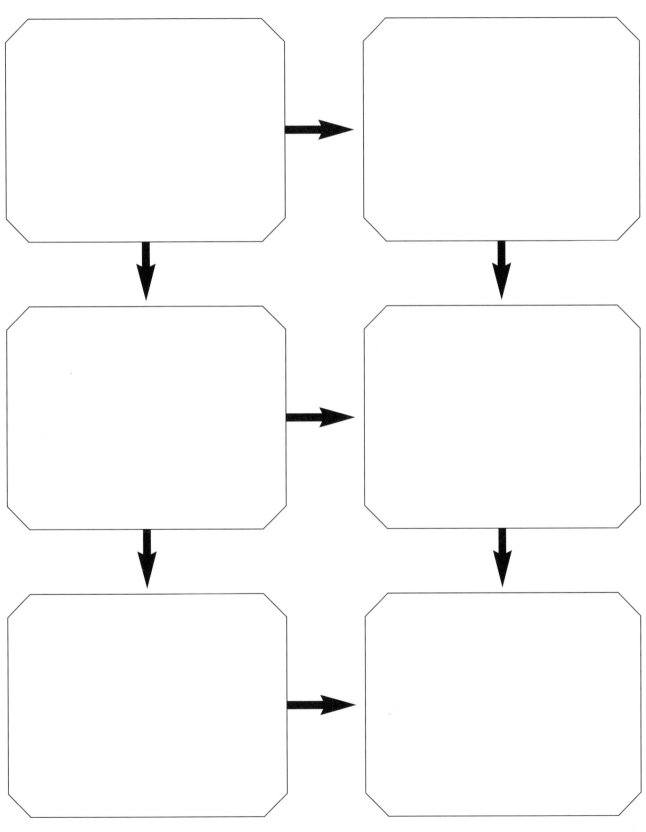

Standards-Based SCIENCE
Graphic Organizers & Rubrics for Elementary Students

Charting Science Skills

Directions to Student:

Complete each of the sentence starters below as well as the activity at the bottom of this rubric.

1. One problem I had in completing this charting exercise was . . .

_____

_____

_____

2. One thing I know I did well on this charting exercise is . . .

_____

_____

_____

3. Something I would tell another student to do when completing a charting exercise like this is . . . _____

_____

_____

4. An idea that came to my mind while doing this charting exercise was . . .

_____

_____

_____

5. If I were to do another charting exercise assignment I would . . .

_____

_____

_____

At the bottom of this page, use pictures, words, icons, symbols, or sketches to tell about something you learned from this charting exercise.

Concept Builder

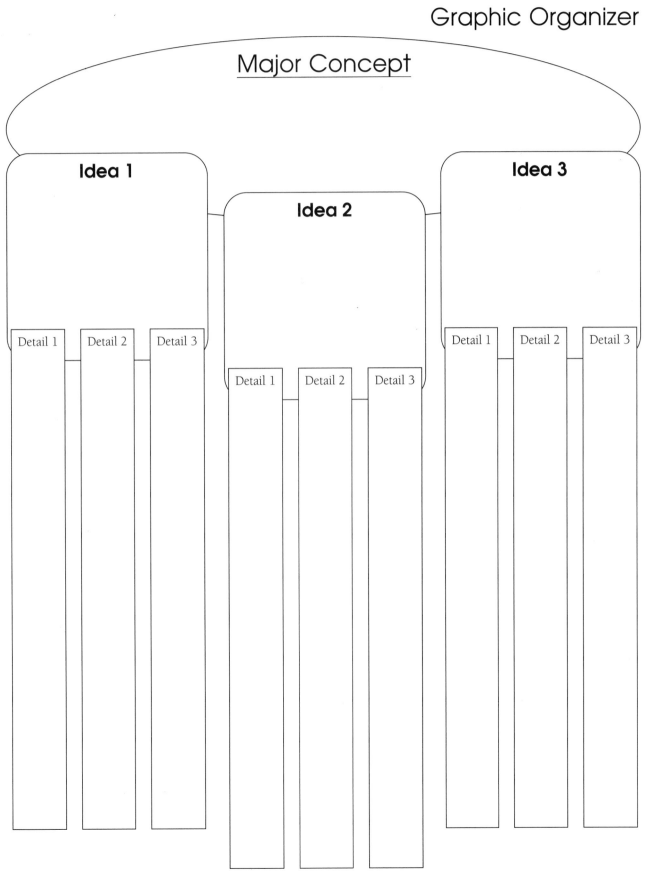

Major Concept

Idea 1

Idea 2

Idea 3

Detail 1 | Detail 2 | Detail 3

Detail 1 | Detail 2 | Detail 3

Detail 1 | Detail 2 | Detail 3

Concept Builder

Rubric

Rating Scale:

3	2	1
Expert	Intermediate	Beginner

Directions to Student:

In the box at the end of each line, write the number that best describes your work.

1. Quality of my concept or big idea in the top circle	☐
2. Quality of my supporting Ideas in the squares below the top circle	☐
3. Quality of my important details or examples in the bottom rectangles	☐
4. Quality of my thinking during this activity	☐
5. Quality of my overall concept builder	☐

Comments by Student: _____

_____

_____

_____

Signed _____ Date _____

Comments by Teacher: _____

_____

_____

_____

_____

Signed _____ Date _____

Standards-Based SCIENCE
Graphic Organizers & Rubrics for Elementary Students

Context Clues

Science Term

Type of Context Clue

- Example or Non-Example
- Compare/Contrast

Text Definition _____

_____

_____

Science Term

Type of Context Clue

- Example or Non-Example
- Compare/Contrast

Text Definition _____

_____

_____

Science Term

Type of Context Clue

- Example or Non-Example
- Compare/Contrast

Text Definition _____

_____

_____

43

Context Clues

Rubric

Rating Scale:

3	2	1
Always	Some of the Time	Never

Directions to Student:

In the box at the end of each line, write the number that best describes your work.

1. I was able to located and identify many different science-related terms during this unit of study.	☐
2. I was able to use context clues to figure out the meanings of the terms.	☐
3. I was able to learn and remember the definitions for each of the terms.	☐
4. I was able to state the definitions of these terms in my own words as needed.	☐

Directions to Student:

Write down the most important science terms that you studied in this unit with your own definition of each word as you understand it.

Science Term   My Definition of Term

1. _____   _____

                             _____

2. _____   _____

                             _____

3. _____   _____

                             _____

4. _____   _____

                             _____

5. _____   _____

                             _____

Cycle Graph

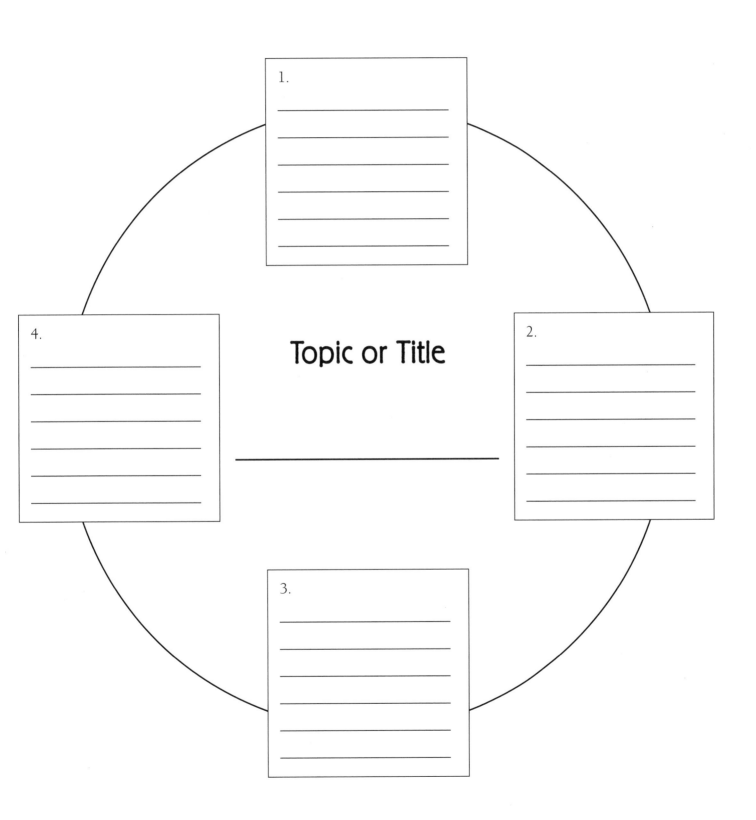

1.

_____
_____
_____
_____
_____

Topic or Title

_____

2.

_____
_____
_____
_____
_____
_____

4.

_____
_____
_____
_____
_____

3.

_____
_____
_____
_____
_____

Cycle Graph

Rubric

Directions to Student:

Place an "x" in the square under the heading that best describes your work.

Rating Scale:	Superb	So-So	Needs Work
1. I understand the concept of "cycle" as it relates to various science topics.			
2. I understand how to choose a science topic that can be explained through a cycle diagram.			
3. I understand how to record the various steps in a cycle of my choice.			
4. I understand how to insert additional items in the cycle if it requires extra steps beyond those available in the cycle graph.			
5. I understand how to construct a cycle graph on my own without help from the teacher.			
6. I understand how a cycle graph could be used in subject areas other than science.			

Comments by Student: _____

_____

_____

_____

Signed _____ Date _____

Comments by Teacher: _____

_____

_____

_____

Signed _____ Date _____

Data Gathering Sheet
for a Scientific Biography

Graphic Organizer

Name of Scientist, Date/Place of Birth, Date/Place of Death

Childhood Experiences

Personal Character Traits/Skills/Interests/Strengths

Problems/Difficulties Encountered and Overcome

Important Discoveries/Contributions/Awards and Tributes

Standards-Based SCIENCE
Graphic Organizers & Rubrics for Elementary Students

Data Gathering Sheet
for a Scientific Biography

Rubric

Rating Scale:

1	2	3
Excellent	Good	Poor

Directions to Student:

In the box at the end of each line, write the number that best describes your work on this activity.

1. I selected an interesting person to write about.	☐
2. I wrote about his/her early childhood and adult experiences.	☐
3. I wrote about his/her personal skills, character traits, interests, and strengths.	☐
4. I wrote about his/her important discoveries and contributions.	☐
5. I wrote about his/her problems and difficulties to overcome.	☐
6. I wrote about his/her special awards/celebrations/tributes.	☐

Comments by Student: _____

_____

_____

_____

Signed _____ Date _____

Comments by Teacher: _____

_____

_____

_____

Signed _____ Date _____

Standards-Based SCIENCE
Graphic Organizers & Rubrics for Elementary Students

Copyright ©2004 by Incentive Publications, Inc.
Nashville, TN.

Discussion Guide

1. What are five facts that you learned about the topic that you are willing to share?

   Fact One _____

   Fact Two _____

   Fact Three _____

   Fact Four _____

   Fact Five _____

   _____

2. What confuses you about the subject?

3. What else would you like to know about the subject?

4. What are some new pieces of information that you have learned on this topic as a result of this discussion?

Discussion Guide

Rating Scale: **1**   **2**   **3**

Always   Sometimes   Never

Directions to Student:

On each of the cards below, in the box provided, write the number that best describes your ability. Then, write a brief comment defending your rating on the lines provided.

---

1. I enjoy participating in group discussion activities.
   COMMENTS:
   _____
   _____
   _____
   _____

---

2. I am a good listener during group discussion activities.
   COMMENTS:
   _____
   _____
   _____
   _____

---

3. I understand how important it is to take an active part in these discussion activities.
   COMMENTS:
   _____
   _____
   _____
   _____

---

4. I am able to answer a set of questions to better prepare myself for these discussion activities.
   COMMENTS:
   _____
   _____
   _____
   _____

---

5. I value the Discussion Guide graphic organizer because it serves me as an agenda to follow during the discussion and as a tool for sharing my ideas during the discussion.
   COMMENTS:
   _____
   _____
   _____
   _____

Event Outcome Graph

	Event 1	Event 2	Event 3	Event 4
Result				
Result				
Result				
Result				
Result				
Result				

Standards-Based SCIENCE
Graphic Organizers & Rubrics for Elementary Students

Event Outcome Graph

Rating Scale: ⬢ 4   ⬢ 3   ⬢ 2   ⬢ 1

Home Run   Third Base   Second Base   First Base

Directions to Student:

In the "bases" below, write the number that best describes your performance.

2. Quality of my overall Event/Outcome Graph

3. Quality of my topic chosen to record a series of scientific events

1. Quality of my related outcomes/results recorded on the vertical axis

4. Quality of my events recorded on the horizontal axis

Comments by Student: _____

_____

_____

Signed _____ Date _____

Comments by Teacher: _____

_____

_____

Signed _____ Date _____

Experiment Form
for Use with Any Science Topic

Graphic Organizer

Activity:_____

Directions to Student:

Write an experiment-related task or question that you will perform for each
of the multiple intelligences listed below:

Verbal/Linguistic
Logical/Mathematical
Visual/Spatial
Body/Kinesthetic
Musical/Rhythmic
Interpersonal
Intrapersonal
Naturalistic

Standards-Based SCIENCE
Graphic Organizers & Rubrics for Elementary Students

Experiment Form
for Use with Any Science Topic

Rubric

Rating Scale: 3   2   1

                        Excellent   Good   Needs Work

Directions to Student:

In the box at the end of each line, write the number that describes your work on this activity. Then, briefly write down what you did for that intelligence area.

1. **Verbal/Linguistic Intelligence**
   What I Did: ☐

2. **Logical/Mathematical Intelligence**
   What I Did: ☐

3. **Visual/Spatial Intelligence**
   What I Did: ☐

4. **Body/Kinesthetic Intelligence**
   What I Did: ☐

5. **Musical/Rhythmic Intelligence**
   What I Did: ☐

6. **Interpersonal Intelligence**
   What I Did: ☐

7. **Intrapersonal Intelligence**
   What I Did: ☐

8. **Naturalistic Intelligence**
   What I Did: ☐

Facts Only!

Main Fact

Supporting Facts

1. _____
   _____
2. _____
   _____
3. _____
   _____
4. _____
   _____
5. _____
   _____
6. _____
   _____

Main Fact

Supporting Facts

1. _____
   _____
2. _____
   _____
3. _____
   _____
4. _____
   _____
5. _____
   _____
6. _____
   _____

Standards-Based SCIENCE
Graphic Organizers & Rubrics for Elementary Students

Facts Only!

Rubric

Rating Scale:

3	2	1
I did Great!	I did OK	I Need Help!

Directions to Student:

In the box at the end of each line, write the number that best describes your work on this activity.

1. I was able to pick out and record the Main Facts in my textbook readings using the Fact Sheet graphic organizer	☐
2. I was able to pick out and record the Main Facts from my Internet research using the Fact Sheet Graphic Organizer.	☐
3. I was able to pick out and record the Main Facts from my reviews of the reference/multimedia sources using the Fact Sheet graphic organizer.	☐
4. I was able to pick out the Supporting Facts in my textbook readings using the Fact Sheet graphic organizer.	☐
5. I was able to pick out the Supporting Facts in my Internet research using the Fact Sheet graphic organizer.	☐
6. I was able to pick out the Supporting Facts from my reviews of the reference/multimedia sources using the Fact Sheet graphic organizer.	☐
7. I was able to use the Fact Sheets as a study guide for a quiz and/or test on the material covered.	☐

Comments by Student: _____

_____

Signed _____ Date _____

Comments by Teacher: _____

_____

Signed _____ Date _____

Standards-Based SCIENCE
Graphic Organizers & Rubrics for Elementary Students

Copyright ©2004 by Incentive Publications, Inc.
Nashville, TN.

Famous Person Chart

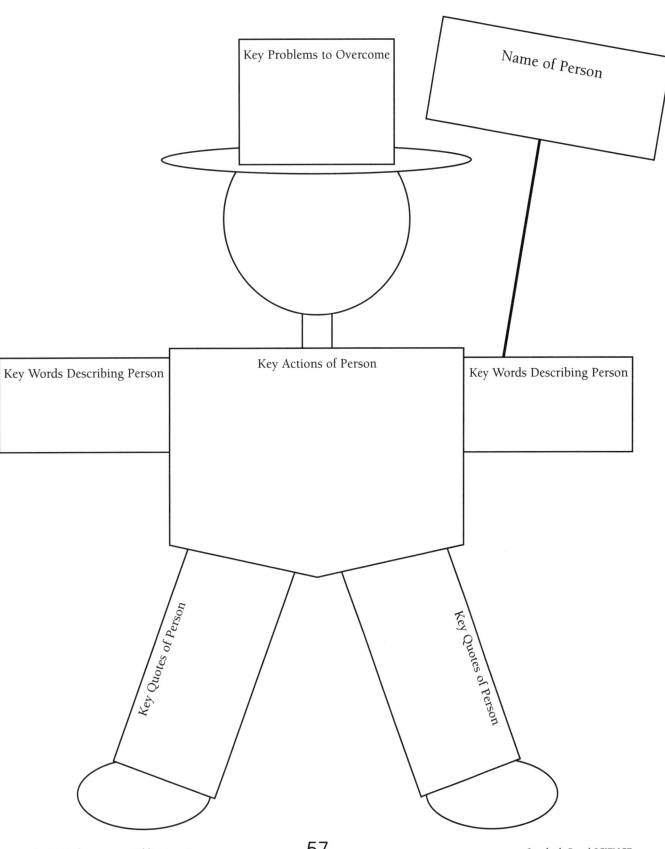

Key Problems to Overcome

Name of Person

Key Words Describing Person

Key Actions of Person

Key Words Describing Person

Key Quotes of Person

Key Quotes of Person

Famous Person Chart

Rating Scale:

| √− | √ | √+ |
| Needs more work | Satisfactory | Excellent |

Directions to Student/Teacher:

In the box at the end of each line, place the correct check mark to show performance on this activity. Then, fill out the evaluation below.

	Student	Teacher
1. Quality of work: Selection process for famous person		
2. Quality of work: Key problems famous person had to overcome		
3. Quality of work: Key words describing person		
4. Quality of work: Key actions of person		
5. Quality of work: Key quotes of person		
6. Quality of work: Research on problems, words, actions, and deeds of person		

The strongest feature of this Famous Person Chart is:

Student _____

Teacher _____

The weakest feature of this Famous Person Chart is:

Student _____

Teacher _____

Recommendation for improvement:

Student _____

_____

Teacher _____

_____

5Ws and How of Scientific Theories, Principles, and Laws

Graphic Organizer

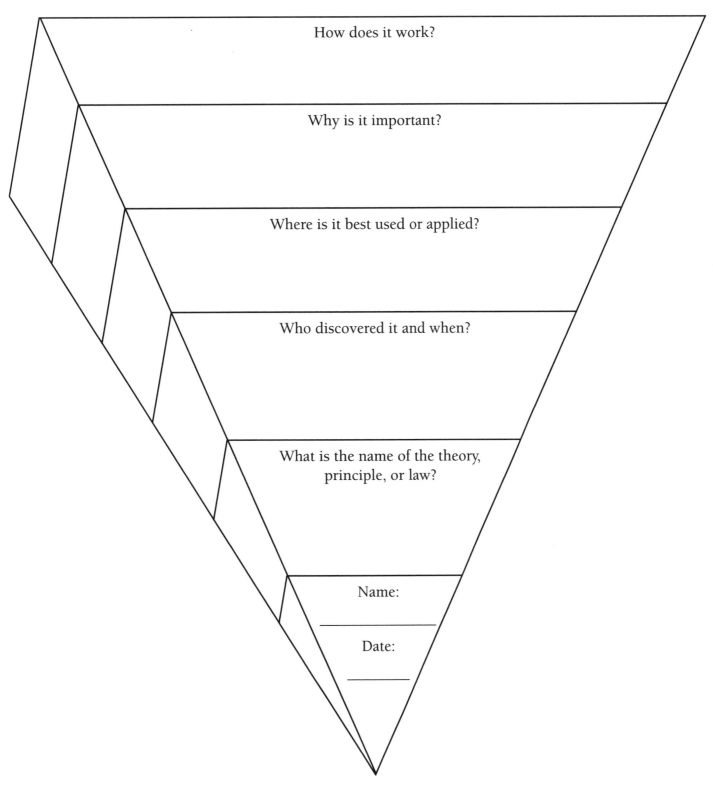

How does it work?

Why is it important?

Where is it best used or applied?

Who discovered it and when?

What is the name of the theory, principle, or law?

Name:

_____

Date:

_____

Standards-Based SCIENCE
Graphic Organizers & Rubrics for Elementary Students

5 Ws and How of Scientific Theories, Principles, and Laws

Rubric

Rating Scale:

3	2	1
Very Well	Fairly Well	Not Well

Directions to Student:

In the triangle at the end of each line, write the number that best describes your performance on this activity.

1. I was able to identify and record the name of the theory, principle, or law.	△
2. I was able to record the name of who discovered it and when.	△
3. I was able to explain where it is best used or applied.	△
4. I was able to discuss why it was important.	△
5. I was able to describe how it works.	△

Comments by Student: _____

_____

_____

_____

Signed _____ Date _____

Comments by Teacher: _____

_____

_____

_____

Signed _____ Date _____

Flowcharting

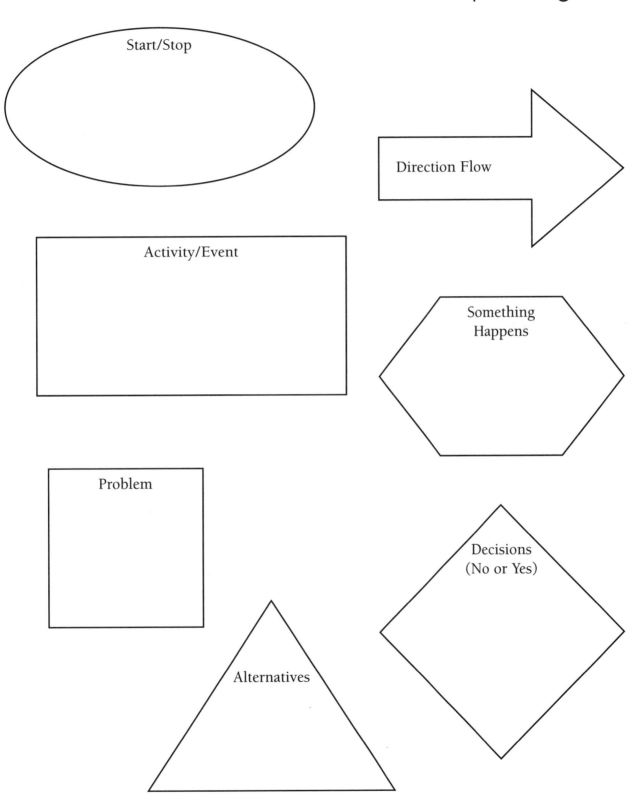

Start/Stop

Direction Flow

Activity/Event

Something
Happens

Problem

Decisions
(No or Yes)

Alternatives

Standards-Based SCIENCE
Graphic Organizers & Rubrics for Elementary Students

Flowcharting

Rating Scale:

➡ 3   ➡ 2   ➡ 1

Always   Sometimes   Never

Directions to Student:

In the arrow at the end of each line, write the number that best describes your work on this activity.

1. The purpose of flowcharting is clear to me.	➡
2. The use of flowcharting symbols makes sense to me.	➡
3. The different shapes, lines, and arrows drawn to indicate different symbols and words are easy for me to use.	➡
4. The sequencing of events to explain a scientific process or phenomenon is important for me to know.	➡
5. The use of a flowchart is helpful to me in understanding a sequence of events.	➡

Comments by Student: _____

_____

_____

_____

_____

Signed _____ Date _____

Comments by Teacher: _____

_____

_____

_____

_____

Signed _____ Date _____

Grade A Science Project Planning Guide

Graphic Organizer

Knowledge: List the materials used in this experiment.

_____   _____

_____   _____

Comprehension: Outline the procedure for conducting the experiment.

1. _____
2. _____
3. _____
4. _____
5. _____

Application: Record data observed and collected during your experiment in chart or graph form.

What I Did	What I Observed
_____	_____
_____	_____
_____	_____

Analysis: Examine your data and draw conclusions.

1. _____
2. _____
3. _____

Synthesis: Create a series of "what if" statements about your data to show things that might be different should variables be changed.

What if . . . _____

What if . . . _____

What if . . . _____

Evaluation: Describe how you would rate the success of your experiment. Establish a set of criteria for measuring the results.

Findings	Measure of Success
_____	_____
_____	_____

Standards-Based SCIENCE
Graphic Organizers & Rubrics for Elementary Students

Grade A Science Project Planning Guide

Rubric

Rating Scale:

3	2	1
Excellent	Fair	Needs Work

Directions to Student:

In the box at the end of each line, write the number that best describes your work on this activity.

1. I did a great job of listing the materials for this experiment. I did a great job of outlining the procedure for conducting this experiment.	☐
2. I did a great job of recording the data (what I did and what I observed) while conducting this experiment.	☐
3. I did a great job of examining my data and drawing conclusions while conducting this experiment.	☐
4. I did a great job of creating and completing a series of "what if" statements related to my data during this experiment.	☐
5. I did a great job of using criteria to judge the results and success of my experiment.	☐

Comments by Student: _____

_____

_____

Signed _____ Date _____

Comments by Teacher: _____

_____

_____

_____

Signed _____ Date _____

Standards-Based SCIENCE
Graphic Organizers & Rubrics for Elementary Students

Idea Organizer

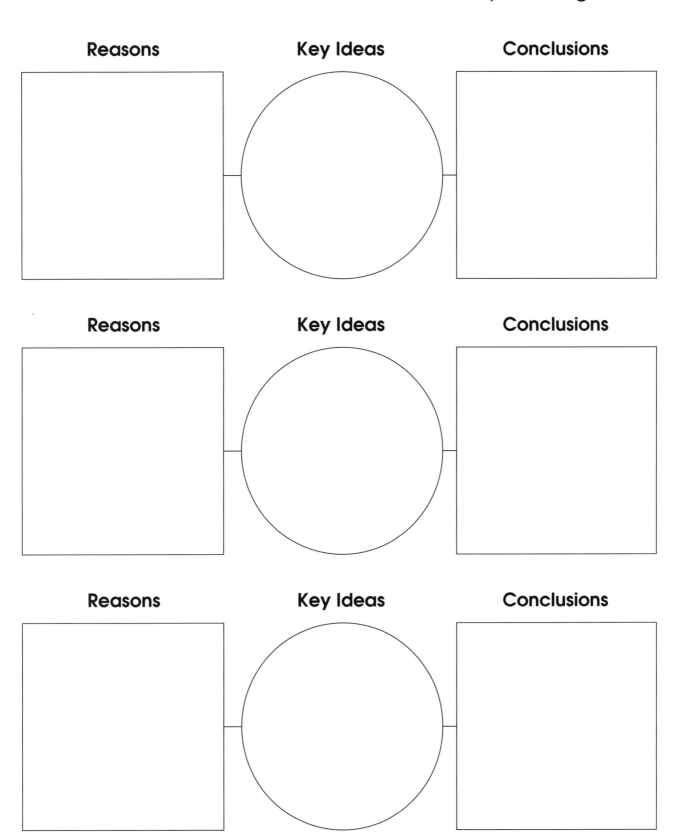

Reasons   **Key Ideas**   **Conclusions**

Reasons   **Key Ideas**   **Conclusions**

Reasons   **Key Ideas**   **Conclusions**

Standards-Based SCIENCE
Graphic Organizers & Rubrics for Elementary Students

Idea Organizer

Rubric

Rating Scale:

3	2	1
Very Successful	Fairly Successful	Not Successful

Directions to Student:

In the box at the end of each line, write the number that best describes your performance on this activity.

1. The idea organizer helped me to organize my ideas. ☐

2. The idea organizer helped me to prepare successfully for a discussion and/or a debate. ☐

3. The idea organizer helped me to think through and record my ideas clearly. ☐

4. The idea organizer helped me to record my reasons logically and clearly. ☐

5. The idea organizer helped me to record my conclusions clearly and accurately. ☐

6. The idea organizer helped me to better understand the discussion/debate topic. ☐

Comments by Student: _____

_____

_____

Signed _____ Date _____

Comments by Teacher: _____

_____

_____

Signed _____ Date _____

Multiple Intelligence Data Organizer
for a Science Project

1. **Verbal/Linguistic Intelligence:** What books, magazines, newspapers, and other print materials are available for you to review?

   _____

   _____

2. **Logical/Mathematical Intelligence:** How can charts, graphs, diagrams, and technology tools help you gather information?

   _____

   _____

3. **Visual/Spatial Intelligence:** What pictures, photographs, maps, videos, posters, and other forms of visuals have information about the topic?

   _____

   _____

4. **Musical/Rhythmic Intelligence:** How might songs, raps, and audiotapes relate to your topic?

   _____

   _____

5. **Body/Kinesthetic Intelligence:** What computer software, Internet web sites, skits, dances, or physical/sporting events could serve you as reliable sources?

   _____

   _____

6. **Interpersonal Intelligence:** What family members, friends, teachers, experts, or community groups/organizations/institutions are there for you to interview in person, by telephone, or through chat rooms?

   _____

   _____

7. **Intrapersonal Intelligence:** What personal experiences, readings, feelings, opinions, or ideas on the topic do you have from which you could pull?

   _____

   _____

8. **Naturalist Intelligence:** How do Mother Nature and wildlife relate to your topic?

   _____

Multiple Intelligence Data Organizer
for a Science Project

Rubric

Rating Scale:

1	**2**	**3**
Excellent	Good	Poor

Directions to Student:

In the box at the end of each line, write the number that best describes your work on this activity.

1. I was able to complete the Verbal/Linguistic Intelligence task successfully. ☐

2. I was able to complete the Logical/Mathematical Intelligence task successfully. ☐

3. I was able to complete the Visual/Spatial Intelligence task successfully. ☐

4. I was able to complete the Musical/Rhythmic Intelligence task successfully. ☐

5. I was able to complete the Body/Kinesthetic Intelligence task successfully. ☐

6. I was able to complete the Interpersonal Intelligence task successfully. ☐

7. I was able to complete the Intrapersonal Intelligence task successfully. ☐

8. I was able to complete the Naturalist Intelligence task successfully. ☐

I did my best work on the _____ Intelligence task because
_____
_____ .

I did my weakest work on the _____ Intelligence task because
_____
_____ .

I enjoyed my work most on the _____ Intelligence task because
_____
_____ .

I enjoyed my work least on the _____ Intelligence task because
_____
_____ .

Standards-Based SCIENCE
Graphic Organizers & Rubrics for Elementary Students

Non-Fiction Book Report Outline

Graphic Organizer

Directions to Student:

Select a non-fiction book on the science topic of your choice and use it to complete the activities below.

Knowledge

1. Record the answers to each of these questions:

   What is the title of this book? _____

   Who wrote the book? _____

   When was the book published? _____

   Where did you locate the book? _____

Comprehension

2. Summarize the main ideas or facts found in the book.

Application

3. Select several key words or terms from the book and classify them in some way

---

Analysis

4. Compare your book with another book on the same topic. How are the books alike and how are they different?

Synthesis

5. Suppose that you were to write a new book on this topic. Create an original book jacket for your masterpiece.

Evaluation

6. Would you recommend the book to anyone else? Give three to five reasons for your choice.

_____

_____

_____

_____

_____

Standards-Based SCIENCE
Graphic Organizers & Rubrics for Elementary Students

Non-Fiction Report Outline

Rubric

Rating Scale:

3	2	1
Fair	Good	Great

Directions to Student:

In the box at the end of each line, write the number that best describes your work on this activity.

1. **Quality of Report Format**
   The report presents relevant topic information neatly written or typed. ☐

2. **Quality of Information**
   Important information is clearly conveyed. ☐

3. **Grammar**
   The report's grammar and spelling is correct. ☐

4. **Details and Descriptions**
   The report is attractive and interesting, and it presents details and descriptions important to the topic. ☐

5. **Graphics/Creativity**
   The report is well-organized in an original and creative manner. ☐

Comments by Student: _____

_____

_____

_____

Signed _____ Date _____

Comments by Teacher: _____

_____

_____

_____

Signed _____ Date _____

Standards-Based SCIENCE
Graphic Organizers & Rubrics for Elementary Students

Copyright ©2004 by Incentive Publications, Inc.
Nashville, TN.

Observation Log

Date: _____ Time: _____

Observation: _____

_____

_____

_____

_____

_____

_____

_____

_____

Date: _____ Time: _____

Observation: _____

_____

_____

_____

_____

_____

_____

_____

_____

Observation Log

Rubric

Rating Scale: A   B   C
             Excellent Work   Good Work   Needs Work

Directions to Student:

In the box at the end of each line, write the letter that best describes your work on this activity.

1. **Appropriateness of Subject:** My subject for the required observations is interesting, important, and manageable. ☐

2. **Quality of My Entries:** My observation entries include important terms, experiences, events, feelings, reactions to observations, summaries, and conclusions on what I see and do. ☐

3. **Details and Descriptions of My Observations:** My observation entries are written using colorful vocabulary and original thought to present details and descriptions in a lively manner. ☐

4. **Grammar:** My observation entries have no errors in grammar or spelling. ☐

5. **Interest:** My observation entries are interesting to read and hold the reader's attention. ☐

6. **Graphics, Drawings, Sketches:** My observation entries are enhanced with relevant graphics, drawings, or sketches as needed. ☐

Some things I would do differently if I were conducting an observation study again are:

_____

_____

_____

_____

_____

_____

Observation Subject: _____

Date Started Observations: _____ Date Completed Observations: _____

Standards-Based SCIENCE
Graphic Organizers & Rubrics for Elementary Students

Outline for Developing a Science Unit

Graphic Organizer

Directions for Student:

Developing a science unit on a topic of your choice is easier than you think. Just choose your topic and then select one or more tasks from each level of Bloom's Taxonomy below to create a teaching and learning unit.

TOPIC _____

Knowledge

1. List five to ten questions that you would like to answer about the topic.
2. Identify five to ten key words or terms related to the topic and write their definitions.
3. Name three to five specific sources for information about the topic.

Comprehension

1. Outline a plan for finding out all you can about the topic.
2. Summarize what you would like to know most about the topic.
3. Describe five to ten ways that you might share acquired information.

Application

1. Interview someone with knowledge of the topic.
2. Make a model to show something important about the topic.
3. Conduct an experiment to demonstrate a key idea related to the topic.

Analysis

1. Compare and contrast some aspect of your topic with that of another topic.
2. Divide your topic into several sub-topics.
3. Conduct your survey to show how others feel about the topic.

Synthesis

1. Create a list of predictions related to the topic.
2. Compose a poem or story about the topic.
3. Design a series of drawings or diagrams to show facts about the topic.

Evaluation

1. Determine the five most important facts you have learned about the topic. Rank them from most important to least important, giving reasons for your first choice.
2. Criticize a resource you used to find out more information about the topic and give at least three recommendations for improving it.

Standards-Based SCIENCE
Graphic Organizers & Rubrics for Elementary Students

Outline for Developing a Science Unit

Directions to Student:

Place an "x" in the space before the correct amount of evidence you have to support your work on this activity.

Title of Unit: _____

Knowledge: Evidence of learned facts, methods, procedures, or concepts.
___ Great Evidence   ___ Ample Evidence   ___ Little Evidence

Comprehension: Evidence of understanding of facts, methods, procedures, or concepts.
___ Great Evidence   ___ Ample Evidence   ___ Little Evidence

Application: Evidence of use of the information in new situations.
___ Great Evidence   ___ Ample Evidence   ___ Little Evidence

Analysis: Evidence of analysis, recognition of assumptions, and evaluation of relevancy of information.
___ Great Evidence   ___ Ample Evidence   ___ Little Evidence

Synthesis: Evidence of putting information together in a new and creative way.
___ Great Evidence   ___ Ample Evidence   ___ Little Evidence

Evaluation: Evidence of acceptance or rejection of information on the basis of criteria.
___ Great Evidence   ___ Ample Evidence   ___ Little Evidence

---

Comments by Student: _____

_____

Signed _____ Date _____

Comments by Teacher: _____

_____

Signed _____ Date _____

Panel Presentation Outline

Graphic Organizer

Topic for Panel _____

Name of Panel Moderator _____

Question 1: _____

Question 2: _____

Question 3: _____

Question 4: _____

Panel Member One

_____

_____

_____

Panel Member Two

_____

_____

_____

Panel Member Three

_____

_____

_____

Panel Member Four

_____

_____

_____

Panel Presentation Outline

Rubric

Rating Scale:

3	2	1
Very Pleased	Somewhat Pleased	Not Pleased

Directions to Student:

In the box at the end of each line, write the number that best describes your work on this activity.

1. The topic I chose for our panel presentation was appropriate and of interest to all panel members and to the members of the audience.	☐
2. I chose three good people to serve on the panel.	☐
3. I picked a good moderator for the panel.	☐
4. I wrote down the most important names and science concepts to be covered by each panel member.	☐
5. I wrote down many quality questions to be covered by the individual panel members.	☐
6. I rehearsed the presentation with panel members and the moderator, focusing on the questions to be answered and the delivery of the information to be shared.	☐
7. I felt the overall panel presentation was well received by the audience because of its clarity and interest.	☐

Here is a compliment I would like to give each of the panel members:

Panel member 1: _____

Panel member 2: _____

Panel member 3: _____

Panel member 4: _____

Moderator: _____

Standards-Based SCIENCE
Graphic Organizers & Rubrics for Elementary Students

Picture/Graph Response Chart

Describe what you see.

Explain what is happening.

Tell why this is happening.

Give reasons why it was chosen for this book.

Picture/Graph Response Chart

Rubric

Rating Scale:

1	2	3
Completely	Somewhat	Not At All

Directions to Student:

In the box at the end of each line, write the number that best describes your work on this activity.

1. I know what this means: "A picture is worth a thousand words." ☐

2. I know how a Picture/Graph Response Sheet can help me to express my thoughts in a meaningful and visual way. ☐

3. I know how to describe what I see in a picture, photograph, illustration, drawing, diagram, chart, or graph that is found in a science textbook or reference book. ☐

4. I know how to explain what is happening in a visual I find in a science textbook or reference book. ☐

5. I know why something is happening in a visual I find in a science textbook or reference book. ☐

6. I know reasons why a visual was chosen for a science textbook or reference book. ☐

Comments by Student: _____

_____

_____

_____

Signed _____ Date _____

Comments by Teacher: _____

_____

_____

_____

Signed _____ Date _____

Standards-Based SCIENCE
Graphic Organizers & Rubrics for Elementary Students

Position Paper Planner

Introductory Paragraph

   1. Eye-catching example, startling statement, personal anecdote, dramatic quotation, unusual data/fact to catch reader's attention:

   2. Thesis Statement:

Body Paragraph One

   1. Topic Sentence:

      2. Supporting Sentence:

      3. Supporting Sentence:

      4. Supporting Sentence:

Body Paragraph Two

   1. Topic Sentence:

      2. Supporting Sentence:

      3. Supporting Sentence:

      4. Supporting Sentence:

Body Paragraph Three

   1. Topic Sentence:

      2. Supporting Sentence:

      3. Supporting Sentence:

      4. Supporting Sentence:

Concluding Paragraph

   1. Concluding sentence based on thesis statement:

   2. Final statement in form of rhetorical question, point to ponder, or basis for further study:

Position Paper Planner

Rubric

Rating Scale:

3	2	1
Strong	Acceptable	Weak

Directions to Student:

In the box at the end of each line, write the number that best describes your work on this activity.

1. **Quality of My Introductory Paragraph:** I wrote an opening statement that immediately caught the reader's attention. I also wrote an effective thesis statement. ☐

2. **Quality of Body Paragraph One:** I wrote an effective topic sentence with three related supporting statements. ☐

3. **Quality of Body Paragraph Two:** I wrote an effective topic sentence with three related supporting statements. ☐

4. **Quality of Body Paragraph Three:** I wrote an effective topic sentence with three related supporting statements. ☐

5. **Quality of Concluding Paragraph:** I wrote a concluding sentence that was based on the thesis statement. I also wrote an effective final statement to bring closure to the position paper planner. ☐

6. **Quality of Overall Position Paper:** I was able to convince others how I felt or reacted to the subject of my position paper planner. ☐

Comments by Student: _____

_____

Signed _____ Date _____

Comments by Teacher: _____

_____

_____

Signed _____ Date _____

Standards-Based SCIENCE
Graphic Organizers & Rubrics for Elementary Students

Copyright ©2004 by Incentive Publications, Inc.
Nashville, TN.

Prediction Chart

Draw

What did you see happen?

Write

_____

_____

_____

_____

_____

_____

Draw

What will happen next?

Write

_____

_____

_____

_____

_____

_____

_____

_____

Draw

What else will happen?

Write

_____

_____

_____

_____

_____

_____

_____

Standards-Based SCIENCE
Graphic Organizers & Rubrics for Elementary Students

Prediction Chart

Directions to Student:

Circle "yes" or "no" at the end of each line to indicate your work on this activity.

1. I chose the perfect topic.	Yes	No
2. My predictions were correct.	Yes	No
3. My drawings were helpful.	Yes	No
4. I understand the value and usefulness of a prediction chart.	Yes	No
5. I would use a prediction chart again.	Yes	No

Comments by Student: _____

_____

_____

_____

_____

_____

Signed _____ Date _____

Comments by Teacher: _____

_____

_____

_____

_____

_____

Signed _____ Date _____

Problem-Solving Tree

Graphic Organizer

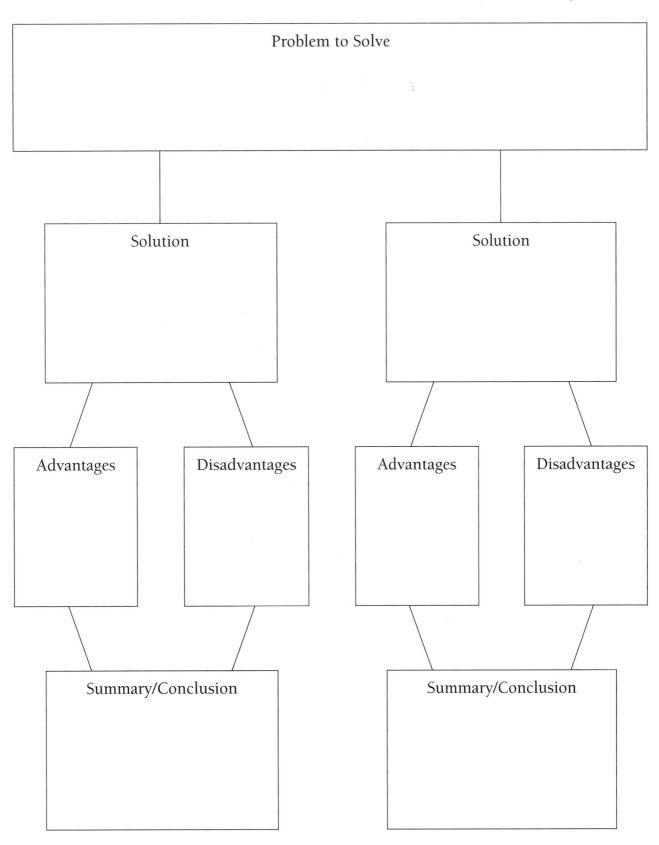

Standards-Based SCIENCE
Graphic Organizers & Rubrics for Elementary Students

Problem-Solving Tree

Rubric

Rating Scale:

4	3	2	1
Full Grown Tree	Smaller Tree	Potted Tree	Small Sapling

Directions to Student:

Use the rating scale above to judge the quality of your Problem-Solving Tree by writing the correct number inside each branch hanging from the tree.

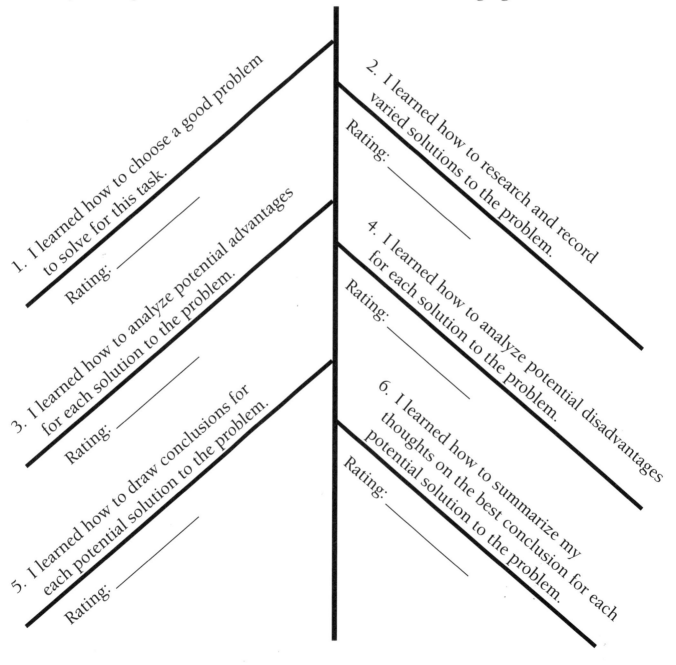

1. I learned how to choose a good problem to solve for this task.

Rating: _____

2. I learned how to research and record varied solutions to the problem.

Rating: _____

3. I learned how to analyze potential advantages for each solution to the problem.

Rating: _____

4. I learned how to analyze potential disadvantages for each solution to the problem.

Rating: _____

5. I learned how to draw conclusions for each potential solution to the problem.

Rating: _____

6. I learned how to summarize my thoughts on the best conclusion for each potential solution to the problem.

Rating: _____

Standards-Based SCIENCE
Graphic Organizers & Rubrics for Elementary Students

Prove the Hypothesis Chart

Hypothesis/Proof/Opinion Chart

Hypothesis:	Proof Statements:

Opinion/Proof Notes and Conclusion

Standards-Based SCIENCE
Graphic Organizers & Rubrics for Elementary Students

Prove the Hypothesis Chart

Rubric

Rating Scale:

A	B	C
Very Well	Somewhat	Not At All

Directions to Student:

In the box at the end of each line, write the number that best describes your work on this activity.

1. I can explain why this graphic organizer is called a Hypothesis Chart.	☐
2. I can record my notes on this chart when forming a hypothesis about a scientific idea, discovery, or experiment.	☐
3. I can write the hypothesis so that it makes sense to the reader and me.	☐
4. I can give statements of proof to support the hypothesis.	☐
5. I can give statements of proof to negate the hypothesis.	☐
6. I can summarize my opinion-proof notes in a concluding paragraph.	☐

My definition of a hypothesis is _____

_____

_____

My statements of proof to support the hypothesis seem to be _____

_____

_____

My statements of proof to negate the hypothesis seem to be _____

_____

_____

My concluding paragraph seems to support _____

_____

_____

Standards-Based SCIENCE
Graphic Organizers & Rubrics for Elementary Students

Research Guide

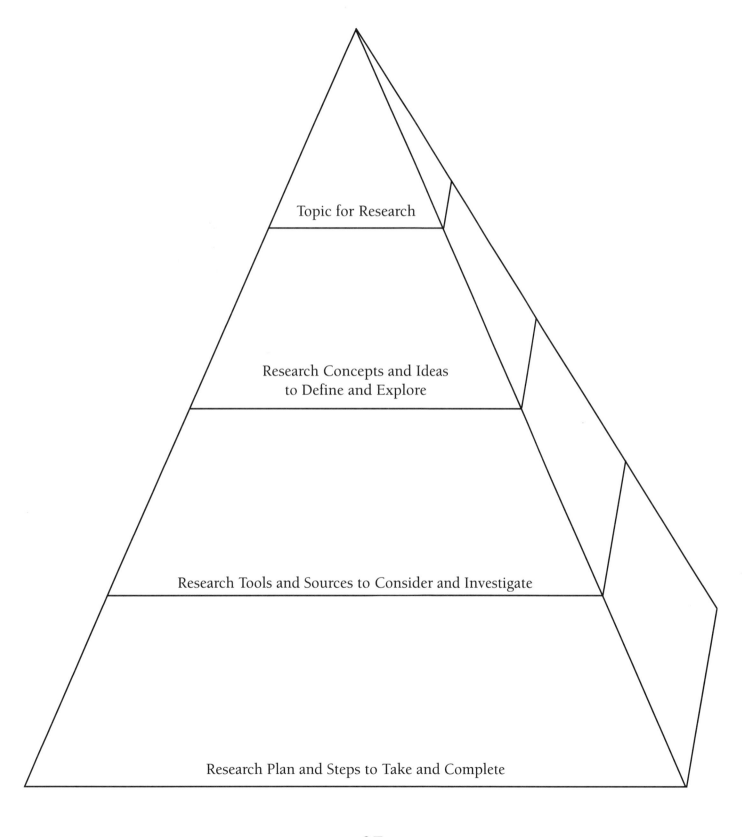

Topic for Research

Research Concepts and Ideas
to Define and Explore

Research Tools and Sources to Consider and Investigate

Research Plan and Steps to Take and Complete

Standards-Based SCIENCE
Graphic Organizers & Rubrics for Elementary Students

Research Guide

Directions to Student:

Place an "x" to indicate how far you got in your work on this activity.

---

1. I selected a science topic that I felt was appropriate and manageable for this research study.

   |————————|————————|————————|————————|
   First Base   Second Base   Third Base   Home Run

2. I met with my teacher to talk about the topic and my ideas for the research study.

   |————————|————————|————————|————————|
   First Base   Second Base   Third Base   Home Run

3. I defined the key concepts and ideas that I wanted to explore as part of my research study.

   |————————|————————|————————|————————|
   First Base   Second Base   Third Base   Home Run

4. I identified the tools and sources to consider and investigate for my research study.

   |————————|————————|————————|————————|
   First Base   Second Base   Third Base   Home Run

5. I developed a comprehensive outline, time line, and set of action steps to implement my research study.

   |————————|————————|————————|————————|
   First Base   Second Base   Third Base   Home Run

6. I successfully completed my research study according to the terms of my plan.

   |————————|————————|————————|————————|
   First Base   Second Base   Third Base   Home Run

7. I enjoyed working on my research study and look forward to doing another one sometime in the future.

   |————————|————————|————————|————————|
   First Base   Second Base   Third Base   Home Run

8. I know my teacher was pleased with the quality of my research study.

   |————————|————————|————————|————————|
   First Base   Second Base   Third Base   Home Run

Research Paper Outline

Graphic Organizer

I. Topic

II. Introduction

III. Background Information

IV. Materials and Sources

V. Resource People

VI. Procedures

VII. Investigations and Results

VIII. Discussion

IX. Conclusion and Summary

X. Bibliography

XI. Appendix

Standards-Based SCIENCE
Graphic Organizers & Rubrics for Elementary Students

Research Paper Outline

Rubric

Rating Scale:

3	2	1
Superior	Acceptable	Not Acceptable

Directions to Student/Teacher:

In the box at the end of each line, write the number that shows performance on this activity. Then, fill out the evaluation below.

	STUDENT RATING	TEACHER RATING
1. Choice of Topic		
2. Quality of Introduction		
3. Completeness of Background Information		
4. Organization of Procedures		
5. Reporting of Investigations and Results		
6. Interest Generated by Discussion		
7. Details in Conclusion and Summary		
8. Accurate Entries in Bibliography		
9. Items in Appendix		
10. Grammar, Punctuation, Spelling		
11. Imagination or Creativity		
12. Evidence of Best Effort		

Comments by Student: _____

_____

Signed _____ Date _____

Comments by Teacher: _____

_____

Signed _____ Date _____

Standards-Based SCIENCE
Graphic Organizers & Rubrics for Elementary Students

Science Project Display Board Plan

Graphic Organizer

Purpose	**Topic**	**Materials**
Problem or Question	**Investigations — Observations**	**Procedures**
Hypothesis	**Results**	**Conclusions**

Standards-Based SCIENCE
Graphic Organizers & Rubrics for Elementary Students

Science Project Display Board Plan

Directions to Student:

After evaluating your performance, place an "x" in the correct box after each question.

	Yes	Maybe	No
1. Did I establish a purpose for this project?	☐	☐	☐
2. Did I address a problem or question in this project?	☐	☐	☐
3. Did I write a hypothesis for this project?	☐	☐	☐
4. Did I choose an appropriate topic for this project?	☐	☐	☐
5. Did I report on my investigations and observations for this project?	☐	☐	☐
6. Did I describe the results for this project?	☐	☐	☐
7. Did I list the materials used for this project?	☐	☐	☐
8. Did I summarize the procedures I followed during this project?	☐	☐	☐
9. Did I explain the conclusions for this project?	☐	☐	☐

Comments by Student: _____

_____

_____

_____

Signed _____ Date _____

Comments by Teacher: _____

_____

_____

Signed _____ Date _____

Science Quilt

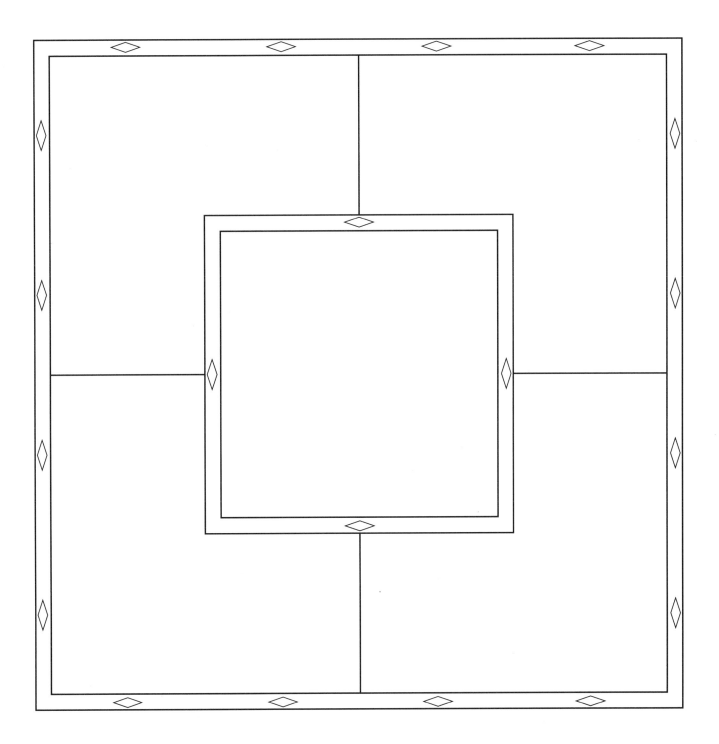

Science Quilt

Rating Scale:

1	2	3
Excellent Work	Good Work	Needs Work

Directions to Student:

In the box at the end of each line, write the number that best describes your work on this activity.

1. I chose a good topic to study. ☐

2. I was able to find five different pieces of information on my topic. ☐

3. I created a repeating drawing/icon for each section of my science quilt organizer. ☐

4. I think my drawings/icons were good ones. ☐

5. I did a great job in reporting information about my topic. ☐

6. I learned a lot on my topic from this activity. ☐

7. I really enjoyed this assignment. ☐

Comments by Student: _____

_____

Signed _____ Date _____

Comments by Teacher: _____

_____

_____

Signed _____ Date _____

Scientific Categories
and Their Relationships

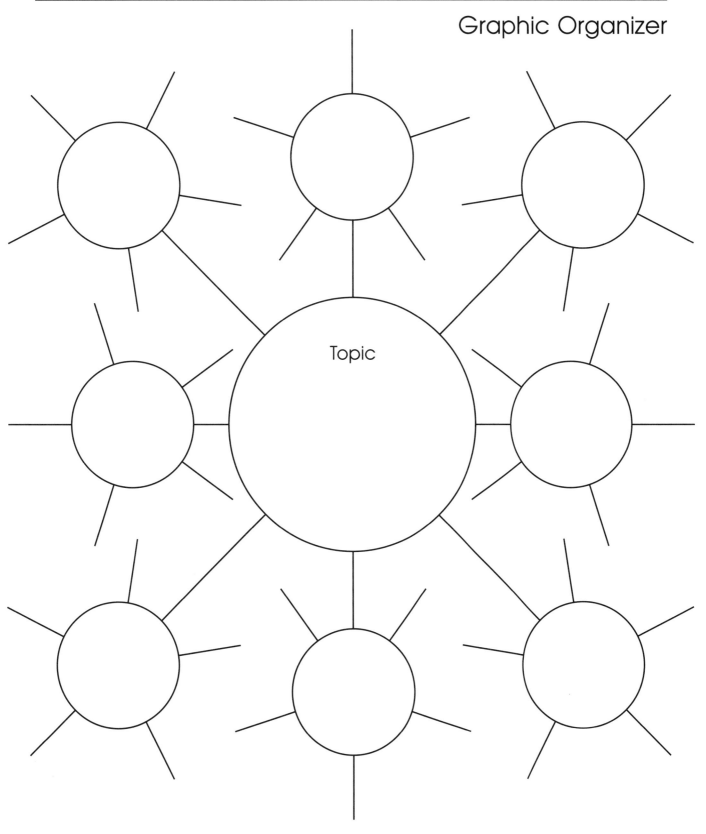

Topic

Standards-Based SCIENCE
Graphic Organizers & Rubrics for Elementary Students

Scientific Categories and Their Relationships

Rubric

Rating Scale:

3	2	1
Great	Good	Poor

Directions to Student:

In the star at the end of each line, write the number that best describes your work on this activity.

1. I chose a good scientific topic for study in this activity.	☆
2. I recorded my topic in the large circle.	☆
3. I listed many subcategories related to my topic in the small circles.	☆
4. I wrote details related to each small circle on the lines of each small circle.	☆
5. I can see a scope and sequence pattern to this organizational structure.	☆
6. I can visually see relationships among all my circles and lines.	☆

The most important thing I learned from this activity was _____

_____

The most challenging part of this activity for me was _____

_____

Something I would do differently next time if I were to repeat this activity would be _____

_____

Some advice I would give others about doing this activity would be _____

_____

Standards-Based SCIENCE
Graphic Organizers & Rubrics for Elementary Students

Scientific Terms Log

Scientific Term	Definition of Term	Illustration/Sentence of Term

Scientific Term	Definition of Term	Illustration/Sentence of Term

Scientific Term	Definition of Term	Illustration/Sentence of Term

Scientific Term	Definition of Term	Illustration/Sentence of Term

Scientific Terms Log

Rubric

Rating Scale:

3	**2**	**1**
Consistently	Most of the Time	Once in a While

Directions to Student:

In the box at the end of each line, write the number that best describes your work on this activity.

1. I have kept up my log on a daily basis.	☐
2. I have recorded scientific terms in my log as I encounter them in my unit of study.	☐
3. I have recorded the definitions of each term using a dictionary, glossary, or chapter definitions.	☐
4. I have either illustrated each term or written it correctly in a sentence.	☐
5. I have increased my scientific vocabulary as a result of this log.	☐
6. I have learned the value of maintaining a scientific terms log for any science unit of study.	☐

The most interesting term for me to define and learn was _____

because _____

_____

The most unusual term for me to define and learn was _____

because _____

_____

The most difficult term for me to define and learn was _____

because _____

_____

The term I am most likely to use in future units of study is _____

because _____

_____

Standards-Based SCIENCE
Graphic Organizers & Rubrics for Elementary Students

Study Guide
for Preparing for a Science Quiz

Graphic Organizer

STUDY GUIDE		
Topics to be Covered 1. Major Topic 2. Sub-topics	**Today's Date** _____ **Quiz Date** _____	**Length/Format of Quiz**

Materials to be reviewed (textbooks, class notes, handouts)

Challenges to be expected and/or questions to answer

My Study Plan

1.

2.

3.

4.

5.

6.

Standards-Based SCIENCE
Graphic Organizers & Rubrics for Elementary Students

Study Guide
for Preparing for a Science Quiz

Directions to Student:

Draw one, two, or three stars in each box below to rate the quality of your work.

	1. I studied all of the major topics for this science quiz to the best of my ability.
	2. I studied all of the sub-topics for this science quiz to the best of my ability.
	3. I reviewed all of the resource/reference materials for this science quiz to the best of my ability.
	4. I reviewed my textbook/class notes and the class handouts for this science quiz to the best of my ability.
	5. I reviewed my in-class and homework assignments for this science quiz to the best of my ability.
	6. I developed a comprehensive study plan for this science quiz, which included all of the above items to the best of my ability.

1. The best time for me to study when preparing for a science quiz is _____

   because _____

   _____

   _____

2. The best sources of information for me to review when preparing for a science quiz are

   _____

   _____

   _____

3. Something I will do better or differently next time when studying for a science quiz is

   _____

   because _____

   _____

Textbook Survey

Fact

Comment/Reaction/Opinion

Question

Fact

Comment/Reaction/Opinion

Question

101

Textbook Survey

Rubric

Rating Scale:

3	2	1
Advanced	Average	Absent

Directions to Student:

In the box at the end of each line, write the number that best describes your work on this activity.

1. I know how to record the main fact given in a paragraph from a textbook chapter.	☐
2. I know how to express a personal comment or reaction to a paragraph from a textbook chapter.	☐
3. I know how to state a personal opinion related to a paragraph from a textbook chapter.	☐
4. I know how to ask myself a question from a paragraph in a textbook chapter that will help me remember an important fact from that paragraph.	☐
5. I know how to survey and write down important information from a textbook selection that I am reading.	☐
6. I know the importance of having textbook survey skills.	☐

Comments by Student: _____

_____

_____

Signed _____ Date _____

Comments by Teacher: _____

_____

_____

Signed _____ Date _____

Standards-Based SCIENCE
Graphic Organizers & Rubrics for Elementary Students

Time Line Template

Graphic Organizer

Topic: _____

Dates	Events	Notes or Comments

Standards-Based SCIENCE
Graphic Organizers & Rubrics for Elementary Students

Time Line Template

Rating Scale:

3	2	1
High Degree	Satisfactory Degree	Not At All

Directions to Student:

In the box at the end of each line, write the number that best describes your work on this activity.

1. I was able to understand the importance of recording important dates when doing a scientific investigation.	☐
2. I was able to record key dates on my time line template.	☐
3. I was able to label specific events that went with each date on my time line template.	☐
4. I was able to extend the time line template as needed.	☐
5. I was able to add important notes or comments where appropriate to do so on my time line template.	☐
6. I was able to explain the data on my time line template to others in the class.	☐

Peer Reactions to my Time Line Template: _____

_____

_____

Teacher Reactions to my Time Line Template: _____

_____

_____

My Reactions to my Time Line Template: _____

_____

_____

Venn Diagram

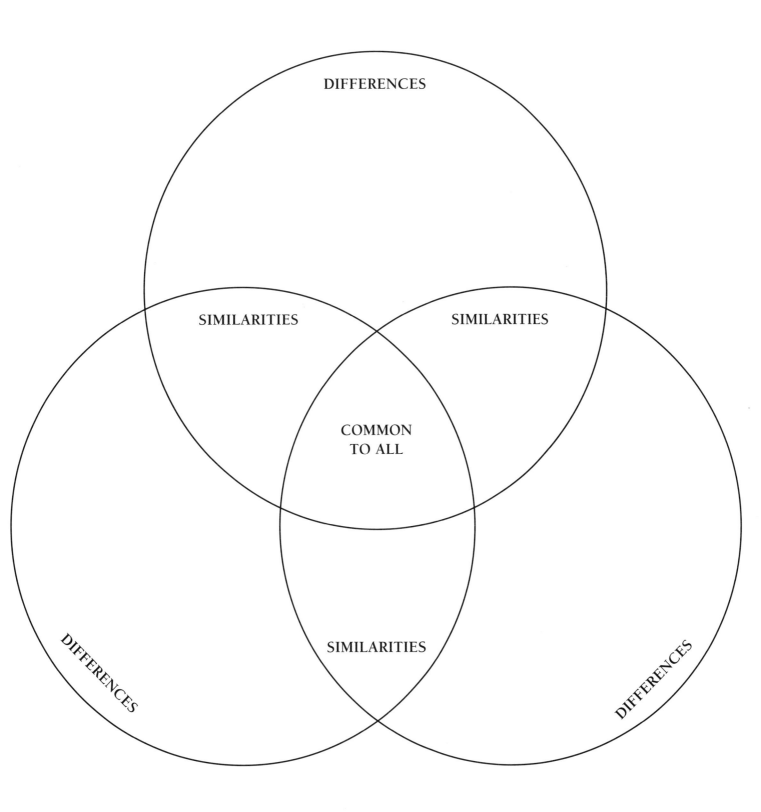

DIFFERENCES

SIMILARITIES   SIMILARITIES

COMMON
TO ALL

DIFFERENCES

SIMILARITIES

DIFFERENCES

Standards-Based SCIENCE
Graphic Organizers & Rubrics for Elementary Students

Venn Diagram

Rating Scale:

1	2	3
Not at All	Somewhat	Completely

Directions to Student:

Write down the correct rating for each of the statements below.

1. I know how many circles make up a Venn diagram.	◯
2. I know the purpose of a Venn diagram.	◯
3. I know where to record the differences on a Venn diagram.	◯
4. I know where to record the similarities on a Venn diagram.	◯
5. I know where to record the elements common to all on a Venn diagram.	◯
6. I know how to explain the interrelationships shown on a Venn diagram.	◯

Comments by Student: _____

_____

_____

_____

Signed _____ Date _____

Comments by Teacher: _____

_____

_____

_____

Signed _____ Date _____

Weather Observation Chart

Graphic Organizer

Weather Observation Log

Date	Time	Temperature	Weather Type	Cloud Cover	Wind Condition	Wind Chill Temperature	Forecast

Weather Symbols

WEATHER TYPE

Rain — R
Thunderstorm — T
Fog — FG
Smog — SMG
Frost — FR
Snow — S

CLOUD COVER

Clear Skies
Partly Cloudy
Cloudy

WIND CONDITIONS

Calm (No air motion)
Breezy (Leaves in motion, water rippled)
Windy (Tree limbs moving, whitecaps on water)
Very Windy (Tree trunks bend, water rough)

Standards-Based SCIENCE
Graphic Organizers & Rubrics for Elementary Students

Weather Observation Chart

Rating Scale:

Sunshine   Cloudy   Rain

Rubric

Directions to Student:

Draw in the correct weather symbol (Sun, Cloud, or Raindrops) for each item below.

1. I know how to identify and record the weather symbols for any given day.	◯
2. I know how to read and record the temperature for any given day.	◯
3. I know how to identify and record the weather type for any given day.	◯
4. I know how to identify and record the cloud cover for any given day.	◯
5. I know how to identify and record the wind condition for any given day.	◯
6. I know how to identify and record the wind chill factor for any given day.	◯
7. I know how to construct and maintain a Weather Observation Chart.	◯

Comments by Student: _____

_____

Signed _____ Date _____

Comments by Teacher: _____

_____

_____

Signed _____ Date _____

Standards-Based SCIENCE
Graphic Organizers & Rubrics for Elementary Students

What, So What, Now What? Chart

Graphic Organizer

Topic of Study/Title _____

Student's Name _____

What?	So What?	Now What?

Standards-Based SCIENCE
Graphic Organizers & Rubrics for Elementary Students

What, So What, Now What? Chart

Rubric

Rating Scale:

■ ■ ■
Very Good

■ ■ □
Good

■ □ □
Not So Good

Directions to Student:

Shade in the number of blocks to show your performance on this activity.

1. I have been able to apply a "What, So What, Now What" Chart to my work.	□ □ □
2. I have been able to record a response to the question: "WHAT" is the meaning of this piece and/or what did I learn from it?	□ □ □
3. I have been able to record a series of responses to the question: "SO WHAT" difference does it make now that I know this, or what is its importance?	□ □ □
4. I have been able to record an answer to the question: "NOW WHAT" can I do to use this information so that it makes a difference in what I know or can do or so I understand how it is important and relates to the major theme of study?	□ □ □

Comments by Student: _____

_____

_____

_____

Signed _____ Date _____

Comments by Teacher: _____

_____

_____

_____

Signed _____ Date _____

Standards-Based SCIENCE
Graphic Organizers & Rubrics for Elementary Students

Appendix

National Science Education Standards
Grades K-4 Science Content

Unifying Concepts and Processes

Standard: As a result of activities in grades K-4, all students should develop understanding and abilities aligned with the following concepts: systems, order, and organization; evidence, models, and explanation; constancy, change, and measurement; evolution and equilibrium; and form and function.

Science as Inquiry

Content Standard A: As a result of activities in grades K-4, all students should develop abilities necessary to do scientific inquiry and understandings about scientific inquiry.

Physical Science

Content Standard B: As a result of their activities in grades K-4, all students should develop an understanding of properties of objects and materials, position and motion of objects, and light, heat, electricity, and magnetism.

Life Science

Content Standard C: As a result of their activities in grades K-4, all students should develop an understanding of the characteristics of organisms, the life cycle of organisms, and organisms and their environments.

Reprinted with permission from National Science Education Standards ©1995 by the National Academy of Sciences. Courtesy of the National Academies Press, Washington D.C.

Earth and Space Science

Content Standard D: As a result of their activities in grades K-4, all students should develop an understanding of properties of earth materials, objects in the sky, and changes in earth and sky

Science and Technology

Content Standard E: As a result of their activities in grades K-4, all students should develop abilities of technological design, understandings about science and technology, and distinguishing between natural objects and objects made by humans.

Science in Personal and Social Perspectives

Content Standard F: As a result of their activities in grades K-4, all students should develop understandings of personal health, characteristics and changes in populations, types of resources, changes in environments, and science and technology in society.

History and Nature of Science

Content Standard G: As a result of activities in grades K-4, all students should develop understanding of science as human endeavor.

Reprinted with permission from National Science Education Standards ©1995 by the National Academy of Sciences. Courtesy of the National Academies Press, Washington D.C.

Planning Matrix

Correlatives: National Science Education Standards as identified by the National Academy of Sciences with activities and projects in Standards-Based Science Graphic Organizers & Rubrics for Elementary Students, Incentive Publications, 2004.

Standards	Graphic Organizers	Rubrics
Unifying Concepts and Processes	31, 33, 35, 37, 39, 41, 45, 49, 51, 53, 55, 59, 61, 63, 65, 67, 69, 71, 74, 77, 79, 83, 87, 89, 93, 95, 97, 99, 101, 103, 105, 109	32, 34, 36, 38, 40, 42, 46, 50, 52, 54, 56, 60, 62, 64, 66, 68, 70, 72, 78, 80, 84, 88, 90, 94, 96, 98, 100, 102, 104, 106, 110
Science as Inquiry	31, 33, 35, 37, 39, 41, 43, 49, 51, 53, 55, 59, 61, 63, 67, 69, 71, 73, 74, 77, 79, 81, 83, 85, 87, 89, 91, 93, 95, 97, 99, 101, 109	32, 34, 36, 38, 40, 42, 44, 50, 52, 54, 56, 60, 62, 64, 68, 70, 72, 74, 78, 80, 82, 84, 86, 88, 90, 92, 94, 96, 98, 100, 102, 110
Physical Science	31, 35, 37, 39, 41, 43, 45, 49, 51, 53, 55, 59, 61, 63, 67, 69, 71, 73, 74, 75, 77, 79, 81, 83, 85, 87, 89, 91, 93, 95, 97, 99, 101, 109	32, 36, 38, 40, 42, 44, 46, 50, 52, 54, 56, 60, 62, 64, 68, 70, 72, 74, 76, 78, 80, 82, 84, 86, 88, 90, 92, 94, 96, 98, 100, 102, 110
Life Science	31, 33, 35, 39, 41, 43, 45, 49, 51, 53, 55, 59, 61, 63, 67, 69, 71, 73, 74, 75, 77, 79, 81, 83, 85, 87, 89, 91, 93, 95, 97, 99, 101, 109	32, 34, 36, 40, 42, 44, 46, 50, 52, 54, 56, 60, 62, 64, 68, 70, 72, 74, 76, 78, 80, 82, 84, 86, 88, 90, 92, 94, 96, 98, 100, 102, 110

Planning Matrix

Correlatives: National Science Education Standards as identified by the National Academy of Sciences with activities and projects in Standards-Based Science Graphic Organizers & Rubrics for Elementary Students, Incentive Publications, 2004.

Standards	Graphic Organizers	Rubrics
Earth and Space Science	31, 33, 35, 39, 41, 43, 45, 49, 51, 53, 55, 59, 61, 63, 67, 69, 71, 73, 74, 75, 77, 79, 81, 83, 85, 87, 89, 91, 93, 95, 97, 99, 101, 109	32, 34, 36, 40, 42, 44, 50, 52, 54, 56, 60, 62, 64, 68, 70, 72, 74, 76, 78, 80, 82, 84, 86, 88, 90, 92, 94, 96, 98, 100, 102, 108, 110
Science and Technology	31, 33, 35, 37, 39, 41, 43, 45, 49, 51, 53, 55, 59, 61, 63, 67, 69, 71, 73, 74, 75, 77, 79, 81, 83, 85, 87, 89, 91, 93, 95, 97, 99, 101, 109	32, 34, 36, 38, 40, 42, 44, 46, 50, 52, 54, 56, 60, 62, 64, 68, 70, 72, 74, 76, 78, 80, 82, 84, 86, 88, 90, 92, 94, 96, 98, 100, 102, 110
Science in Personal and Social Perspectives	31, 35, 37, 39, 41, 45, 47, 49, 51, 53, 55, 63, 65, 67, 69, 74, 75, 79, 83, 87, 89, 91, 93, 95, 97, 99, 101, 103, 105, 109	32, 36, 38, 40, 42, 46, 48, 50, 54, 56, 64, 66, 68, 70, 76, 80, 84, 88, 90, 92, 94, 96, 98, 100, 102, 104, 106, 110
History and Nature of Science	31, 35, 39, 41, 45, 47, 49, 53, 55, 57, 63, 65, 67, 69, 74, 75, 79, 87, 89, 91, 93, 95, 97, 99, 101, 103, 109	32, 36, 40, 42, 46, 48, 50, 54, 56, 58, 64, 66, 68, 70, 76, 80, 88, 90, 92, 94, 96, 98, 100, 102, 104, 110

Reprinted with permission from National Science Education Standards ©1995 by the National Academy of Sciences. Courtesy of the National Academies Press, Washington D.C.

Standards-Based SCIENCE
Graphic Organizers & Rubrics for Elementary Students

GUIDELINES
for Using Graphic Organizers

1. Graphic organizers can be used for curriculum planning, helping students process information, and as pre- or post-assessment tasks. Determine which types of graphic organizers are best for each purpose.

2. Graphic organizers are a performance-based model of assessment and make excellent artifacts for inclusion in a student portfolio. Decide which concepts in your discipline are best represented by the use of these organizers.

3. Use graphic organizers to help students focus on important concepts while omitting extraneous details.

4. Use graphic organizers as visual pictures to help the student remember key ideas.

5. Use graphic organizers to connect visual language with verbal language in active learning settings.

6. Use graphic organizers to enhance recall of important information.

7. Use graphic organizers to provide student motivation and relieve student boredom.

8. Use graphic organizers to show and explain relationships between and among varied content areas.

9. Use graphic organizers to make traditional lesson plans more interactive and more appealing to the visual learner.

10. Use graphic organizers to break down complex ideas through concise and structured visuals.

11. Use graphic organizers to help students note patterns and clarify ideas.

12. Use graphic organizers to help students better understand the concept of "part to whole."

13. Emphasize the use of graphic organizers to stimulate creative thinking.

14. Make sure there is a match between the type of organizer and the content being taught.

15. Make sure that using a graphic organizer is the best use of time when teaching a concept.

16. Use a wide variety of graphic organizers and use them collaboratively whenever possible.

Standards-Based SCIENCE
Graphic Organizers & Rubrics for Elementary Students

Copyright ©2004 by Incentive Publications, Inc.
Nashville, TN.

GUIDELINES
for Using Rubrics

1. The rubric reflects the most important elements of an assigned task, product, or performance and enables both student and teacher to depict accurately the level of competence or stage of development of individual students.

2. The rubric is planned to augment, reinforce, personalize, and strengthen (but not replace) the assessment program mandated by curriculum guidelines or system requirements.

3. The rubric encourages student self-evaluation and can be shared with students prior to beginning the task so that students know exactly what represents quality work.

4. The rubric has two components which are: (1) characteristics or criteria for quality work on a specific task, and (2) determination of the specific levels of proficiency or degrees of success for each part of a task.

5. The rubric is designed to explain more concretely what a child knows and can do and is less subjective and more focused than other means of student evaluation.

6. Rating scales have been created to evaluate student performance. Easy-to-use weights for each answer make the results clear and specific.

7. If the rubric is holistic, it consists of paragraphs arranged in a hierarchy so that each level of proficiency has a paragraph describing factors that would result in that specific level.

8. If the rubric is analytical, it consists of a listing of criteria most characteristic of that task accompanied with the degrees of success for each model listed separately beside or under each criterion.

9. Samples of student work have been studied to determine realistic attributes common to varied performances at different levels of proficiency. These attributes have been translated into descriptors for the degrees of proficiency and to establish a rating scale to delineate those degrees of proficiency.

10. The rubric is accompanied by carefully planned opportunities for meta-cognitive reflections to provide for self-assessment observations completely unique to the students' own learning goals, expectations, and experiences.

Standards-Based SCIENCE
Graphic Organizers & Rubrics for Elementary Students

The Graphic Organizer Report Assessment

Rubric

Rating Scale: 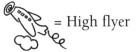 = High flyer   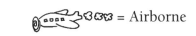 = Airborne   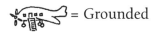 = Grounded

---

1. **Quality of Report Format:**
   The graphic organizer selected is an
   appropriate choice for use in the report.   Rating: _____

2. **Quality of Information:**
   The information shows significant research on the topic.   Rating: _____

3. **Grammar:**
   Spelling, grammar, and punctuation
   have been checked carefully.   Rating: _____

4. **Interest:**
   The different subtopics fit together well
   and highlight the main points of the topic.   Rating: _____

5. **Graphics/Creativity:**
   The graphic organizer fits the information to be organized
   and is used in a unique and/or creative way
   to convey the information as efficiently as possible.   Rating: _____

Comments by Student: _____

_____

_____

Signed _____ Date _____

Comments by Teacher: _____

_____

_____

Signed _____ Date _____

Overall Rating: _____

Signed _____ Date _____

Calendar for Use of Graphic Organizers

	Monday	Tuesday	Wednesday	Thursday	Friday
Knowledge/ Comprehension	Use magazines, newspapers, and your textbooks to find a wide assortment of graphic organizers. State the main purpose or type of information given in each graphic organizer.	List all the different ways you can think of that we use graphic organizers in our everyday lives. Consider how they are used in department stores, in airports, in supermarkets, and in sports.	Define graphic organizers using your own words, then use a dictionary. Compare the two definitions.	Take the information in one of the graphic organizers and rewrite it in another form.	Classify your collection of graphic organizers in at least three different ways. Explain the rationale for your grouping.
Comprehension/ Application/ Analysis	Compare a chart and a table. In a good paragraph, summarize how they are alike and how they are different.	Collect information about junk foods popular with your age group. Use a Venn Diagram to show your results.	Construct a flowchart to show how you would like to spend a perfect 24-hour day.	Survey the students in your class to determine their favorite television show. Show your results on a graphic organizer.	How is a graphic organizer like a road map? Like a blueprint? Like a photograph?
Analysis/ Synthesis	Study your collection of graphic organizers. Determine some types of data and subject matter that are best depicted by a graphic organizer.	Diagram a flowchart for constructing a graph or a table on grade point averages for students in your science class.	Write a story that has one of the following titles: "The Magic Web" "Who Needs A Concept Map?" "Who Moved My Graphic Organizer?"	Draw a picture or write a paragraph to illustrate one of these expressions: "He turned the tables on me!" "It's time to chart your course!"	Design a poster about a school project, event, or activity that uses a graphic organizer as part of its message.
Evaluation	Develop a set of recommendations for students to follow when constructing a high-quality graphic organizer.	Develop a set of criteria for judging the worth or value of a given graphic organizer. Apply this criteria to each unit of your collection. Rank order your graphic organizers, from most effective to least effective.	Defend this statement: Presenting a graphic organizer is the best way to convince a friend of something.	Design a poster of graphic organizers. Find as many different examples as you can. Mount examples on poster board and write three insightful questions about each one.	Explain how each of the following people might use graphic organizers in their work: computer programmer, teacher, mall manager, astronaut, brain surgeon, and carpenter.

Standards-Based SCIENCE
Graphic Organizers & Rubrics for Elementary Students

Gardner's Multiple Intelligences

Did you know there are eight different types of intelligence and that each of us possesses all eight, although one or more of them may be stronger than others? Dr. Howard Gardner, a researcher and professor at the Harvard Graduate School of Education, developed the Theory of Multiple Intelligences to help us better understand ourselves and the way we acquire information in school.

Try to rank order the eight intelligences below as they best describe the way *you* learn, with "1" being your weakest intelligence area and "8" being your strongest intelligence area. Try to think of examples and instances in the classroom when you were successful on a test, assignment, activity, or task because it was compatible with the way you like to learn.

_____ 1. **Linguistic Intelligence:** Do you find it easy to memorize information, write poems or stories, give oral talks, read books, play word games like Scrabble and Password, use big words in your conversations or assignments, and remember what you hear?

_____ 2. **Logical/Mathematical Intelligence:** Do you find it easy to compute numbers in your head and on paper, to solve brain teasers, to do logic puzzles, to conduct science experiments, to figure out number and sequence patterns, and to watch videos or television shows on science and nature themes?

_____ 3. **Spatial Intelligence:** Do you find it easy to draw, paint, or doodle, work through puzzles and mazes, build with blocks or various types of buildings sets, follow maps and flowcharts, use a camera to record what you see around you, and prefer reading material with many illustrations?

_____ 4. **Body/Kinesthetic Intelligence:** Do you find it easy to engage in lots of sports and physical activities, move around rather than sit still, spend free time outdoors, work with your hands on such things as model-building or sewing, participate in dance, ballet, gymnastics, plays, puppet shows or other performances, and mess around with finger painting, clay, and papier-maché?

_____ 5. **Musical Intelligence:** Do you find it easy to play a musical instrument or sing in the choir, listen to favorite records or tapes, make up your own songs or raps, recognize off-key recordings or noises, remember television jingles and lyrics of many different songs, and work while listening to or humming simple melodies and tunes?

_____ 6. **Interpersonal Intelligence:** Do you find it easy to make friends, meet strangers, resolve conflicts among peers, lead groups or clubs, engage in gossip, participate in team sports, plan social activities, and teach or counsel others?

_____ 7. **Intrapersonal Intelligence:** Do you find it easy to function independently, do your own work and thinking, spend time alone, engage in solo hobbies and activities, attend personal growth seminars, set goals, analyze your own strengths and weaknesses, and keep private diaries or journals?

_____ 8. **Naturalist Intelligence:** Do you find yourself extremely comfortable and happy outdoors, have a desire to explore and observe the environment, use outdoor equipment such as binoculars easily, and want to understand how natural systems evolve and how things work?

Standards-Based SCIENCE
Graphic Organizers & Rubrics for Elementary Students

Bloom's Taxonomy of Cognitive Thinking Skills

Bloom's Taxonomy of Cognitive Thinking Skills is a model that can help you learn how to think critically and systematically. (*Taxonomy* is another word for *structure* or *schemata*.) This taxonomy provides a way to organize thinking skills into six levels. The first level is the most basic, or simplest, level of thinking, and the last level is the most challenging, or most complex, level of thinking.

KNOWLEDGE LEVEL:

Students thinking at this level are asked to memorize, remember, and recall previously learned material. Some common verbs or behaviors for this level are: define, list, identify, label, name, recall, record, draw, recite, and reproduce.

COMPREHENSION LEVEL:

Students thinking at this level are asked to demonstrate their ability to understand the meaning of material learned and to express that meaning in their own words. Some common verbs or behaviors for this level are: explain, describe, summarize, give examples, classify, find, measure, prepare, re-tell, reword, rewrite, and show.

APPLICATION LEVEL:

Students thinking at this level are asked to use learned material in a situation different from the situation in which the material was taught. Some common verbs or behaviors for this level are: apply, compute, construct, develop, discuss, generalize, interview, investigate, model, perform, plan, present, produce, prove, solve, and use.

ANALYSIS LEVEL:

Students thinking at this level are asked to break down material (ideas and concepts) into its component parts so that the organization and relationships between parts is better recognized and understood. Some common verbs or behaviors for this level are: compare and contrast, criticize, debate, determine, diagram, differentiate, discover, draw conclusions, examine, infer, search, survey, and sort.

SYNTHESIS LEVEL:

Students thinking at this level are asked to put together parts of the material to form a new and different whole. Synthesis is the exact opposite of analysis. Some common verbs or behaviors for this level are: build, combine, create, design, imagine, invent, make-up, produce, propose, and present.

EVALUATION LEVEL:

Students thinking at this level are asked to judge the value of material (a statement, novel, poem, research finding, fact) for a given purpose. All judgments are to be based on a set of clearly defined criteria whose outcomes can be defended or validated. Some common verbs or behaviors for this level are: assess, critique, defend, evaluate, grade, judge, measure, rank, recommend, select, test, validate, and verify.

Criteria for Creating Your Own Rubric

Excellent

My portfolio, project, or task
1. is complete.
2. is well-organized.
3. is visually exciting.
4. shows much evidence of multiple resources.
5. shows much evidence of problem solving, decision making, and higher-order thinking skills.
6. reflects enthusiasm for the subject.
7. contains additional work beyond the requirements.
8. communicates effectively what I have learned in keeping with my learning objectives.
9. includes highly efficient assessment tools and makes ample provisions for meta-cognitive reflection.
10. has identified many future learning goals in keeping with my own needs and interests.

Good

My portfolio, project, or task
1. is complete.
2. is well-organized.
3. is interesting.
4. shows some evidence of multiple resources.
5. shows some evidence of problem solving, decision making, and higher-order thinking skills.
6. reflects some interest for the topic.
7. contains a small amount of work beyond the requirements.
8. communicates some things I have learned in keeping with my learning objectives.
9. includes effective assessment tools and reflective comments.
10. has identified some future learning goals in keeping with my own needs and interests.

Needs Improvement

My portfolio, project, or task
1. is incomplete.
2. is poorly organized.
3. is not very interesting to others.
4. shows little or almost no evidence of multiple resources.
5. shows little or almost no evidence of problem solving, decision making, and higher-order thinking skills.
6. reflects little interest in the subject.
7. contains no additional work beyond the minimum requirements.
8. communicates few things that I have truly learned in keeping with my objectives.
9. includes few examples of self assessment tools and reflective comments.
10. has identified no future learning goals in keeping with my own needs and interests.

Standards-Based SCIENCE
Graphic Organizers & Rubrics for Elementary Students

Copyright ©2004 by Incentive Publications, Inc.
Nashville, TN.

Performance, Project, or Task Independent Study Contract

Title _____

Topic _____

Beginning date of work_____

Planned completion/delivery date _____

Goals and/or learning objectives to be accomplished_____

_____

Statement of problems to be researched/studied _____

_____

Format _____

Information/data/resources needed _____

_____

Technical help needed_____

_____

Special equipment and/or materials needed _____

_____

Visual aids and/or artifacts planned_____

_____

Intended audience_____

Method of assessment_____

Student Signature _____ Date: _____

Teacher Signature _____ Date: _____

Standards-Based SCIENCE
Graphic Organizers & Rubrics for Elementary Students

Williams' Taxonomy of Creative Thought

FLUENCY

Enables the learner to generate a great many ideas, related answers, or choices in a given situation.

Sample Cue Words: Generating oodles, lots, many ideas.

FLEXIBILITY

Lets the learner change everyday objects to generate a variety of categories by taking detours and varying sizes, shapes, quantities, time limits, requirements, objectives, or dimensions in a given situation.

Sample Cue Words: Generating varied, different, alternative ideas.

ORIGINALITY

Causes the learner to seek new ideas by suggesting unusual twists to change content or by coming up with clever responses to a given situation.

Sample Cue Words: Generating unusual, unique, new ideas.

ELABORATION

Helps the learner stretch by expanding, enlarging, enriching, or embellishing possibilities that build on previous thoughts or ideas.

Sample Cue Words: Generating enriched, embellished, expanded ideas.

RISK TAKING

Enables the learner to deal with the unknown by taking chances, experimenting with new ideas, or trying new challenges.

Sample Cue Words: Experimenting with and exploring ideas.

COMPLEXITY

Permits the learner to create structure in an unstructured setting or to build a logical order in a given situation.

Sample Cue Words: Improving and explaining ideas.

CURIOSITY

Encourages the learner to follow a hunch, question alternatives, ponder outcomes, and wonder about options in a given situation.

Sample Cue Words: Pondering and questioning ideas.

IMAGINATION

Allows the learner to visualize possibilities, build images in his or her mind, picture new objects, or reach beyond the limits of the practical.

Sample Cue Words: Visualizing and fantasizing ideas.

Standards-Based SCIENCE
Graphic Organizers & Rubrics for Elementary Students

Suggestions for Using Graphic Organizers to Integrate Science into the Total Curriculum

1. Use concept webs or other advanced organizers to explain scientific ideas as they relate to historical events or current happenings.
   Example: Give a speech on pollution or endangered species.

2. Construct flowcharts or diagrams to show processes for completing a specific task related to gathering and disseminating facts and/or information about a scientific issue of concern to people of your age.
   Example: Use a flowchart to plan and develop a research project on conserving our natural resources for the next generation.

3. Design a puppet show storyboard that shows parts of an important event currently affecting global warming, world population, or some other scientific topic of social significance. Remember that a storyboard does not attempt to show all of the scenes in a story, but merely serves as an outline for the major people, places, and events.

4. Design an explanatory chart to show an audience the relationships, sequences, or positions that exist within an institution, group, or collection of data. Consider any topic for this chart, from the types of food chains in natural habitats, to the interactions of countries in sharing technological advances.

5. Use one or more graphic organizers to prepare a presentation. Some graphic organizers to consider are a Concept Builder, a Storyboard, a Venn diagram, a Fishbone, or a Flowchart. This type of presentation is designed to appeal to a person's ability to reason or to a person's ability to feel emotions. Arrange your arguments so that they:

   (1) ask a question and then answer it,
   (2) relate an anecdote, observation, or experience,
   (3) state a fact or statistic.

6. Use a Book Report organizer to plan a report on a biography of a famous scientific person. As you prepare the report, think about your reactions to the events in the historical figure's life that please or bother you, situations that surprise or dazzle you, and obstacles that challenge or disappoint you.

7. Use Venn diagrams to compare and contrast people, places, and socially significant scientific happenings being studied.
   Example: Compare and contrast the development of Alexander Graham Bell's invention of the telephone with the development of the process of pasteurization discovered by Louis Pasteur.

8. Construct line graphs, picot graphs, bar graphs, or circle graphs to organize and present data related to scientific observations, research findings, or community poll results.

9. Use time lines to establish the chronology of important scientific events such as the sequence of events leading up to man landing on the moon, the history of the AIDS virus, or the development of the computer.

10. Identify cause-and-effect situations and construct a cause-and-effect chart to show the sequence and impact.
    Example: Graphically show the influence of technology in today's schools on the workplace of tomorrow.

Standards-Based SCIENCE
Graphic Organizers & Rubrics for Elementary Students

BIBLIOGRAPHY
of Related Incentive Publications Products

202 Science Investigations
by Marjorie Frank

Basic/Not Boring Grades K-1: Science
by Imogene Forte and Marjorie Frank

Basic/Not Boring Grades 2-3: Science
by Imogene Forte and Marjorie Frank

Basic/Not Boring, Grades 4-5:
Human Body & Health
by Imogene Forte and Marjorie Frank

Basic/Not Boring, Grades 4-5: Science
by Imogene Forte and Marjorie Frank

Basic/Not Boring, Grades 4-5: Science Concepts
& Processes
by Imogene Forte and Marjorie Frank

Basic/Not Boring, Grades 4-5: Science Investigations
by Imogene Forte and Marjorie Frank

Basic/Not Boring, Grades 4-5: Problem Solving
by Imogene Forte and Marjorie Frank

Cooperative Learning Guide & Planning Pak
by Imogene Forte and Joy MacKenzie

Creative Science Experiences for the Young Child
(English and Spanish Editions)
by Imogene Forte and Joy MacKenzie

Curriculum and Project Planner for Integrating
Learning Styles, Thinking Skills,
and Authentic Assessment, Revised Edition
by Imogene Forte and Sandra Schurr

Drumming to the Beat of a Different Marcher
by Debbie Silver

Ecology Green Pages
by the Kids' Stuff People

Endangered Species
by Shirley Cook

Environmental Bulletin Boards
by Lynn Brisson

Environmental Impact
by Shirley Cook

Five-Minute Warm-Ups for Elementary Grades,
Revised Edition
by Bea Green, Sandra Schlichting,
and Mary Ellen Thomas

Graphic Organizers and Planning Outlines
by Imogene Forte and Sandra Schurr

I've Got Me and I'm Glad
by Cherrie Farnette, Imogene Forte,
and Barbara Loss

Including the Special Needs Child
by Grace Bickert

Instant Science for Primary Grades
by Sam Ed Brown

Internet Adventures
by Catherine H. Cook
and Janet M. Pfeifer

Internet Quest
by Catherine H. Cook
and Janet M. Pfeifer

Learning Through Research
by Shirley Cook

Learning to Learn
by Gloria Frender

Rain Forest
by Shirley Cook

Science Bulletin Boards
by Imogene Forte and Mary Ann Pangle

Science Yellow Pages
by the Kids' Stuff People

Standards-Based Language Arts Graphic
Organizers and Rubrics for Elementary Students
by Imogene Forte and Sandra Schurr

Standards-Based Math Graphic Organizers
and Rubrics for Elementary Students
by Imogene Forte and Sandra Schurr

Standards-Based Social Studies Graphic Organizers
and Rubrics for Elementary Students
by Imogene Forte and Sandra Schurr

Student Planner and Study Guide for
Science Success
by Imogene Forte and Sandra Schurr

INDEX

Standards-Based SCIENCE
Graphic Organizers & Rubrics for Elementary Students